Braceville Elementary School
District # 75
Braceville, Ill. 60407

DATE DUE			

HIGHSMITH 45-220

HERO OF TWO SEAS

Hero of Two Seas

THE STORY OF
MIDSHIPMAN THOMAS MACDONOUGH

by Charles G. Muller

Illustrated by John Flynn

DAVID McKAY COMPANY, Inc.   NEW YORK

HERO OF TWO SEAS

LIBRARY OF CONGRESS CATALOG CARD NUMBER: 68-26822

MANUFACTURED IN THE UNITED STATES OF AMERICA

Typography by Charles M. Todd

VAN REES PRESS   •   NEW YORK

To my godson, Anthony V. Lynch:

THIS STORY comes to you from Thomas Macdonough's own diary and logs and from Navy Department records of American sailors who fought French privateers in the Caribbean and Barbary pirates in the Mediterranean.

Midshipman Macdonough trained under some of our greatest sea captains. His hard-earned experience enabled him later to defeat an entire British fleet, to help us win our Second War of Independence, and to become *Commodore* Thomas Macdonough.

Quite a man, Tony!

CHARLES G. MULLER

Westport, Connecticut

CONTENTS

CONTENTS

HERO OF TWO SEAS

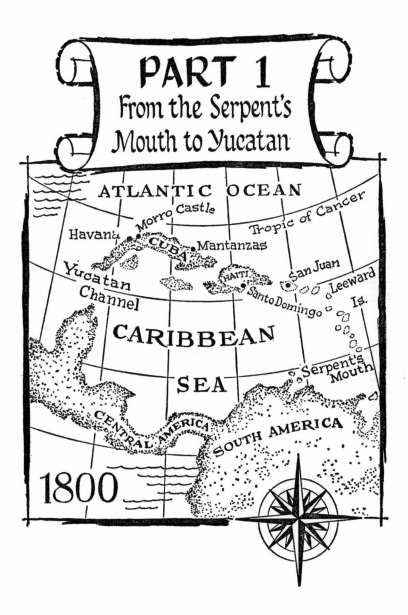

PART 1
From the Serpent's Mouth to Yucatan

ATLANTIC OCEAN

Morro Castle

Tropic of Cancer

Havana

CUBA

Mantanzas

Yucatan Channel

HAITI

San Juan

Santo Domingo

Leeward Is.

CARIBBEAN

SEA

Serpent's Mouth

CENTRAL AMERICA

SOUTH AMERICA

1800

☆☆☆ CHAPTER 1

The rising sun of Saturday morning, 8 February 1800, brought no warning that before noon Thomas Macdonough would encounter three surprises destined to make this the most important day of his seventeen years.

Opening his eyes slowly, Tom glanced across the chilled bedroom at his still sleeping fifteen-year-old brother Sam, shivered into pants and shoes, and shut the slightly open window.

In winter's early light, flat Delaware country stretched stark and cold. But five miles east of where Tom looked out of the brick family homestead, tall ships reached down Delaware Bay toward the seven seas. And in his mind's eye he saw the warm Caribbean and the blue Mediterranean. How much longer must he wait to sail them?

He dabbed at his face in front of the bedroom's corner washstand, and combed his curly reddish hair. Suddenly full of bounce and ready to help his sister Hester start breakfast, he loped downstairs to the kitchen just ahead of her.

A year older than Tom, Hester had his light blue eyes and wide mouth, lips tipped up at the corners in a lurking smile. She also had his strong build; but while he stood a straight and impressive six feet, she stood only three inches over five. Since the marriage of three older sisters—Lydia, Hannah, and

3

Mary—she had cared for the family, which included twelve-year-old Jane, ten-year-old John, and Joseph who was eight. Their mother had died eight years before, their father five.

"I heard you shut your window a long time ago," she said, tying a gingham apron at her waist.

"I just *have* to look out when I first get up," Tom admitted, fanning fireplace embers into flame. Then—the same question he'd asked hourly for days: "Do you think the Secretary of the Navy will appoint me a midshipman?"

Hester went right on with her breakfast chores. "You're like every man I ever heard of! Can't wait to see the world."

"Do you think he'll accept me?"

Hester shook her head as if in despair, and hugged him. "Of course he will! I just hate the thought of your leaving us, like Jim."

"Sam can do almost everything around the farm," Tom pointed out. "He'll give you as much attention as I have."

Though Hester's eyes sparkled, she didn't reply. Humming softly as she moved about the kitchen, she set out oatmeal, cream, sugar, biscuits, butter, and tea.

Eating, Tom tried to talk about the day's chores. But out came the ubiquitous question:

"What makes you so sure he'll accept me?"

Hester pretended bewilderment. "Who'll accept you . . . for what?"

"The Secretary of the Navy! For—Oh, stop it, Hes! I'm serious. Why *should* he appoint me?"

For the thousandth time, Hester assured him.

"Because you've got a United States senator and a member of the state House of Representatives sponsoring you . . . Dr. Henry Latimer and Caesar Augustus Rodney."

Tom looked as though he doubted their abilities in a matter of such importance.

"And," Hester went on, "President Adams certainly remembers that Father served in the Revolutionary War, and that Uncle James died in it, and that Uncle Micah fought the Indians before them. And Mr. Adams must have heard how Jim helped Captain Truxton and *Constellation* defeat the French in *L'Insurgente* last year!"

Hester obviously intended to keep Tom's mind on the practical facts of the situation. Truly, he stemmed from good stock. His Grandfather James had left Ireland in 1730 to set up here —in the village of The Trap—as a physician. His father, a major in the Revolution, had served in Delaware's General Assembly, ending up as a justice of the Court of Common Pleas. Besides all this, Tom had arrived in the world on the very day that General George Washington resigned his military commission into the custody of Congress—23 December 1783.

Tom conceded that the Secretary of the Navy of the United States couldn't overlook such a background. But he also realized that Benjamin Stoddert must have a great many affairs of state to attend to in the Navy Department office at Philadelphia. Tom ran over a few in his mind.

In 1797, resenting the fact that America would not join in her war on England, France had begun to prey on American ships in the West Indies. French privateers had captured three hundred and forty United States merchantmen, in many cases cruelly treating the unlucky crews, and finally had dared make captures in American harbors. Whereupon Congress had acted for five million outraged citizens and America entered on an undeclared war.

Next year, Captain Richard Dale took ship *Ganges* to patrol the American coast. Captain Thomas Truxton followed quickly in frigate *Constellation,* and Captain Stephen Decatur, Sr. took out corvette *Delaware.* Converted merchantmen had joined three squadrons of such men-of-war to patrol the West Indies and to hammer French cruisers wherever found in the Caribbean Sea.

But, Tom wondered, did any of these American ships have

room for another midshipman? Might the French surrender
before he had a chance to fight? If only he'd been old enough
to go on board *Constellation* with Jim! Why hadn't Jim written
more about the big battle with that French frigate? Had another French cruiser captured or killed him?

Hester roused Tom from his meditations, handing him a
pencil-written list, and watched him come back to earth with
a thud.

"Please get these groceries during the morning," she said.
"They can wait until the Wilmington stage arrives. You can
look for your Navy Department letter at the same time."

In mid-morning, Tom crossed the dirt road to the general
store where he occasionally clerked. Over the highway between
house and store, horse-drawn stages carried passengers and
mail twenty-five miles north to the state capital at Wilmington
and one hundred and seventy-five miles south to the Delaware
peninsula's tip at Cape Charles.

The store's proprietor went outside to fill a container with
oil for a white-haired colored man named Uncle Fred, from
back country, while Tom gathered Hester's supplies. When the
front door banged, Tom looked around. Zerah Coffin stomped
into the store. Tom ducked behind the pot-bellied iron stove.

He and his older brother had nicknamed this bearded sailor
Zero because, as Jim put it, "He'll always amount to absolutely
nothing." Zero not only disliked the nickname but he'd bitterly
hated both Macdonoughs since the time he'd gone to bed with
a simple cold and got up to discover they'd left a pine coffin at
his door. Zero had sworn to beat them up. But he never got up
courage to take James on. Nor did he find a chance to tackle
Tom when his brother wasn't around. And while Zero waited,
Tom grew tall and very strong.

Shoving past Uncle Fred now, Zero Coffin pounded a ham-
like fist on the counter.

"Hey you, Hank!" he shouted to the proprietor. "I'm sailin'

today—mate on schooner *Phoebe*—and I want some chawin' tobaccer before the northbound stage comes in."

The store owner hurried through the back door with Uncle Fred's oil, which he put on the counter.

For no reason but sheer meanness, Zero shoved the can out of his way. Upsetting, it spilled and drenched Uncle Fred. As the old colored man tried unhappily to wring oil out of a pants leg, the proprietor protested.

"You shouldn't have done that, Zerah!"

Zero's upper lip rode up over yellow teeth in a malicious grin. "Shut up and find me that tobaccer," he said. "I don't want to miss gettin' to New Castle. I'm headin' for Africa to pick up some of Uncle Fred's nigger relatives."

At mention of slaving, Tom Macdonough's pounding heart presaged the first of the day's adventures. He rose from behind the stove, reached for Zero's pea-jacket collar with his left hand, drove his right fist into the sailor's bearded face, and lunged across the counter as the store door opened to let in the northbound stage driver. So that Tom's tackle carried Zero out into the road almost under the stage's wheels.

In February's deep and sticky mud, Zero Coffin took from Tom the beating he'd so often promised to give—took it despite a seven-year age advantage, despite a twenty-five-pound weight advantage, despite long experience in dirty fighting.

As from a distance, Tom finally heard a voice.

"That's enough! He's licked. Couldn't have done a better job of it myself."

In Navy blues, weather-tanned, James Macdonough held out his hand.

Tom's happy smile faded as he encountered the second of the day's surprises. For the tip of the cane in his brother's left hand rested on the ground beside a second tip. James Macdonough had returned from the Caribbean with a wooden leg.

"Oh, Jim!"

As the stage carried mud-smeared Zero Coffin toward New

Castle and the slave coast of Africa . . . as Tom tried to accept the fact that his brother had come home crippled . . . the southbound stage arrived with an official-looking letter.

Tom read his first naval orders:

> Philadelphia
> Navy Department
> 5th February 1800

Sir:
The President having appointed you a Mid-shipman in the Navy I enclose your warrant.

You will take the enclosed oath and return it to this office, and hold yourself in readiness to enter the service immediately when called upon.

Your pay and emoluments will commence from the date of your letter of acceptance.

> I am, sir, yr. obed. Servt.
> Benjamin Stoddert

☆☆☆ CHAPTER 2

A man in need of action, Midshipman Thomas Macdonough chafed under the onerous task of standing by for sea duty. In the first days after his brother's homecoming, his mind churned up pictures of Zero Coffin whipping blacks in *Phoebe*'s hold, of surgeons in a gory cockpit sawing Jim's leg, of too-busy Secretary Stoddert forgetting to assign new officers to their ships.

Soon, however, he began to curb his impatience. Calming down, he found as he stayed close to Jim that the Navy had transformed his brother from an impetuous youth into a man he'd like to copy, a man of confidence and poise.

As Jim quietly answered a question here, let fall an amusing story there—at the same time that he unobtrusively lifted head-of-the-household responsibilities from Tom's shoulders onto his own—Tom got a feel of what the Navy would expect of him. He pressed for details of the life, particularly of active combat.

Finally Jim gave an eyewitness account of the famous American-French naval battle, but made the part about his leg brief "because it was a rough business."

He told how 36-gun *Constellation,* on patrol to protect American trading vessels, sailed through tropic sunshine on station between St. Kitts and Porto Rico. With Nevis Island five leagues distant "like a blue cloud on the water," Jim related, a large ship came into sight "south and away." *Constellation* brought home her tacks, and bore down. The stranger hung out the tricolor, shortened sail, and fired a gun to windward in challenge. Captain Truxton recognized her for 36-gun *L'Insurgente,* fastest ship in the French navy.

Jim made the ensuing action seem very short.

"A midshipman named Porter and I had charge of marines in the foretop, with muskets, to shoot down on the enemy's deck when we closed. As *Constellation* let *L'Insurgente* have full broadsides, the Frenchman returned a hearty fire, mostly through our rigging. One of her shots sliced the fore-topmast above the cap, and smashed my foot. If the mast went, all headsail would come down in a tangle, the ship would fly upwind out of control, and the Frenchman would rake and ruin us.

"So Davy Porter had me lowered to the deck while he stayed aloft to cut loose the yards at the slings. We won the fight after about an hour with only three wounded, including me."

Jim had refused to come home until the wound fully healed and toughened ... until a Navy carpenter at Norfolk cut a cup-like stump of wood and lined it with soft and spongy leather ... until, with practice, he could walk with comfort on his new leg.

"Funny how things worked out," he joked. "I wanted to stay in the Navy but they couldn't use me. Davy Porter wanted out, and he's still in—even after calling Captain Truxton a tyrant to his face!"

"Is Captain Truxton as tough as they tell?"

"He sees to it that every man knows his job and attends to it. Anyway," Jim went on, "when Davy blurted out that he couldn't stand the Old Man's tongue-lashings, Captain Truxton got red in the face—nearly popped his white wig overside. 'Why, you young dog!' he bellowed. 'Don't you know that every time I swear at you, you go up another round on the ladder of promotion? You'll never leave the Navy if I can help it.' Davy made lieutenant soon after."

Tom listened, dreaming.

"I'll make lieutenant pretty fast, too, I think."

Jim guffawed.

"Don't count on it."

"Why not?"

"Because you'll have so much to learn, and you won't find short cuts. It takes time to make a good officer."

"Then I want to begin learning while I wait for my orders." Tom watched the expressions that crossed his brother's face. Surprise, pleasure.

"Good! We'll start right now."

They did, with Hester and the family's youngsters listening

eagerly and watching with awe as Tom's training took shape. Under Jim's tutoring, Tom learned:

1. How to act as a midshipman . . .
2. How to command as an officer . . .
3. How to rig a ship . . .
4. How to sail a boat.

First, however, he wanted to know what Navy Secretary Stoddert meant in his letter by "emoluments."

"Wages, including an allowance for food," said Jim. "A midshipman gets nineteen dollars a month pay and one food ration a day, worth twenty cents."

As Tom's eyes lighted, Jim deflated him: "A ship's carpenter gets *twenty* dollars a month and *two* rations a day."

When Jim started on lesson No. 1—how to act as a midshipman—Tom cut in. "I know all those. I—"

"Name them!"

Tom saluted sharply, as if on *Constellation*'s quarter-deck. "First, no—"

"Say 'sir' when you address an officer!"

Tom saluted again, but couldn't keep his face straight.

"Wipe that smile off your face, boy!"

"Yes, *sir*," Tom said, at attention.

Jim stood stiff and stern, hands behind his back. "Recite the duties of a midshipman," he ordered.

"First, *sir*," Tom began from a good memory, "no regular duties . . ."

"Which means run errands," Jim amplified, with a trace of a smile.

"Second, *sir,* execute all orders . . ."

"Which means, bear the brunt for most of the lieutenants' wrong instructions."

"Third, *sir,* merit fostering care of officers . . ."

"Meaning," said James, "don't let anybody's horseplay make you lose your sense of humor."

"Fourth, sir," Tom recited, "keep journals . . ."

"That means copy the ship's log blindly."

"Fifth, sir, study naval tactics."

"And *that,* my boy, means you've got to learn everything by observation and never give up hope of becoming a commodore!"

Though he laughed easily with Tom about a midshipman's duties on a man-of-war, Jim went to great lengths in lesson No. 2—how to command as an officer—to picture the manner in which *Constellation's* captain handled his seamen. Thomas Truxton, it appeared, had a way with men—a salty philosophy—that helped the new Navy surprise the French with American derring-do.

Tom learned Truxton's tenets by heart:

Care for your men . . . see that each understands his duty . . . exact instant obedience . . . superintend everything . . . practice daily with gun and sail.

"The Old Man shaped *Constellation's* officers and men into a fighting machine with a soul," Jim declared. "Sailors broidered *Constellation* in great big letters on their hats and told the world that our two-decker could lick any three-decker. Officers like Lieutenant John Rodgers hoped for a chance to take our 36 guns alongside France's best 50-gun ship."

Lesson No. 3—how to rig a ship—proceeded while weather remained cold and wet.

Morning, noon, and night for the better part of two months, Tom got his initiation into the mysteries of knotting, bending, and splicing . . . until he could point a line, work a monkey's fist, and mouse a stay like an able-bodied seaman. With the children looking on whenever they could get away from helping Hester with kitchen chores, he built a full-rigged model of *Constellation* under Jim's direction.

"When you learn every spar and line on this model," said Jim, "you can hold your head up with the best on any Navy ship." He added, "Just remember always to pay for your footing."

"What's that?"

"First time you visit a ship's mast top, treat all hands to a glass of grog."

After Tom could name each separate item of the frigate's rigging and tell how it functioned, Jim pulled the model to pieces.

"Now put it together—by yourself!"

Tom froze for several seconds. He looked at Jim in panic.

"That's an order, boy!"

Of a sudden Tom relaxed. Though he didn't know how far he'd get, he took a first step. He winked at Hester, who viewed the scene with feminine detachment, and went to work on the seemingly insoluble puzzle of spars, lines, and blocks. His outward assurance amazed his small-fry audience, and the way his memory and hands cooperated amazed him too.

He re-rigged the model with speed that, he could see, surprised Jim. But he got no praise.

"Do it again!" Jim ordered. And again. And again.

Tom put the model together so many times that he finally came to believe he could rig the actual frigate to satisfy even Captain Truxton. Whereupon Jim produced a length of white canvas.

"Lay this out and cut it for a new suit of sails. Then turn it all in correctly."

When, after long weeks on lesson No. 3, Tom set up for the last time he received an approving nod.

"Now I'll teach you to sail," said Jim.

On a sunny mid-April Sunday morning after Hester and the youngsters had gone off to church, Tom loaded a battered rowboat into the back of an old Macdonough spring wagon and drove to the shore where Drawyers Creek runs into Delaware Bay. En route Jim announced that lesson No. 4—how to sail a boat—would keep Tom out on the bay every day until time to join his ship.

"That means forever," Tom growled. "The Navy's forgotten I exist!"

"They promised you pay and emoluments," Jim pointed out realistically. "Someone's got you on record."

With a sapling mast, a single sail lateen rigged like a Navy gunboat, and a board hanging over each side to keep Tom's flat-bottomed craft from sliding sidewise, *Connie Too* bore little resemblance to *Constellation*. Tom felt he'd waste every hour he had to spend in her. He'd fished the bay since boyhood; he already knew how to sail, he protested.

Jim cheered him up, and changed his mind about *that*.

"You couldn't spend your time better," Jim pointed out. "Because once you get a real feel of wind and water through *this* tiller, you'll have a magic tough on a ship's wheel."

Tom gradually took heart, and had fun. Keeping *Connie Too* in motion proved to be like nothing he'd ever experienced in larger sailboats. He had to use all the skill at his command to move her through the water with any speed.

A good thing, too, that he'd learned to swim years before. Because Jim ordered him out no matter how hard the wind blew or how high the waves rolled and, in one week, he capsized three times in three straight days.

"I'm developing enough muscles in my arms and shoulders," he told Hester one blustery afternoon as he dried out in the warm kitchen after pushing his water-filled rowboat back to shore, "to swim down to the Caribbean whenever Secretary Stoddert finds a ship for me there!"

By the middle of May, in fair weather and foul, Tom could make *Connie Too* take anything that wind and waves could conjure up.

Jim finally gave him four words of encouragement:

"I think you'll do."

While Tom went to school, Hester's agile fingers sewed for him. With twelve-year-old Jane's help, they'd run up a dozen ruffled-front white linen shirts. They'd also recut and refitted two of Jim's blue coats. And one evening, after supper, Hester and Jane presented a seagoing wardrobe to Tom, making a little ceremony of it for the benefit of the children who had sworn to keep the remaking of the uniforms secret until Hester and Jane had completed them.

Standing before his excited family in full dress, Midshipman Thomas Macdonough—overwhelmed—accepted compliments with pleasure and pride. His beautiful dress coat had short lapels, a standing collar with a diamond of gold lace on each side, and six buttons with buttonholes worked in gold thread. His single-breasted blue vest had flaps but no buttons to the pockets. With the coat and vest he wore blue breeches, black stockings, low-cut silver-buckled shoes. He carried a gold-laced cocked hat.

Jim slapped him jovially on the back.

"How do you feel?"

"Like a commodore."

"You'll get over it by the time you make lieutenant. Nobody can tell a sailor by his clothes!"

For ordinary wear, Tom had a short coat without gold lace. His overcoat, of finest hard wool, came from England—for, in a moment of feeling rich, Jim had bought it from a British lieutenant in need of cash to entertain a Virginia lady friend. As with the uniforms, Hester had cut the overcoat to fit Tom as if originally tailored for him.

Midshipman Macdonough now had, he appreciated, as fine a preparation for a career in the United States Navy as loving care could provide—training that would please a Truxton and a wardrobe fit for a captain. He lacked only one essential—orders to sea.

These finally arrived:

> Philadelphia
> Navy Department
> 15 May 1800

Sir:
The Ship *Ganges* will be at New Castle in a day
or two. You will wait there & on her arrival place
yourself under the command of Capt. Mullowney.

> I am, etc.
> Charles Washington Goldsborough
> By order Secretary of the Navy

P.S. You are entitled to your pay and emoluments
from 17 February 1800 & Purser of the *Ganges*
upon showing him this will pay you from that date.

Not only a midshipman, but a wealthy one!
Though Tom did not learn of it until later, the Navy
Secretary had dispatched orders that same day to Stephen
Decatur, Jr., four years older than Tom and already a lieu-
tenant:

> Sir:
> You will place yourself on board the
> Brig *Norfolk,* under the command of
> Lieut. Calvert.

Tom's path would cross Decatur's in the Caribbean and
recross it in the Mediterranean.

☆☆☆ CHAPTER 3

Midshipman Thomas Macdonough, boarding the New Castle stage, was pulled two ways—sad to be bidding his family goodby but anticipating the new friends he'd make.

Deep down he felt the excitement of entering upon a future in which he might, with the basic qualities he believed he had, play a part in shaping his country's destiny. Jim had encouraged that feeling, supplying an infinite variety of naval lore and tradition which Tom absorbed like a sponge. By way of parting, his brother had said, "You'll do all right, Tom, because you know how to get along with people and know how to concentrate on a job. Just remember what Captain Truxton told us—'A most minute attention to duty is the making of a good officer.'"

For a while, as passengers watched the grave expression on his face and noted the easy, graceful way he held himself, Tom meditatively looked out a stage window. He tried not to put such a word as patriotic to his feelings, because it made him feel self-conscious. But no other word covered what made his heart beat faster with every hoofbeat of the galloping horses.

Jim had described very dramatically President Adams's launching of the Federal Navy just two years ago. Champion of freedom of the seas—whether this was threatened by France or England—John Adams had voiced America's feelings when he said to the new Navy's first captains:

"Let Mahomet, or the Pope, or Great Britain say what they will, mankind will act the part of slaves and cowards if they suffer any nation to usurp dominion over the ocean or any portion of it."

To keep American shipping routes open, ten United States frigates already sailed along the Atlantic Coast and in the Caribbean Sea. Faster and heavier than any rival frigate afloat, they could go into action on their own terms.

This had come about because Philadelphia shipbuilder Joshua Humphreys, draughtsman William Doughty, and young shipwright Josiah Fox had pooled their talents. To the bulk of the French razee (the beshaven) they had imparted the speed of the Baltimore clipper. Into these brand-new frigates they had put 24-pounder batteries previously carried only by line-of-battle ships. Tom wanted to sail in them all.

Right now, however, he had orders for 24-gun *Ganges,* no frigate of 44 guns by a long shot. Laid down in Philadelphia as a merchantman in 1795, "built by no one in particular" as the saying went, bought in 1798 and converted into a Navy cruiser, this patchwork craft had earned the reputation of being a comfortable, roomy, excellent sea boat. She ran fast, scarcely rolled, and almost always had dry decks. Reports had it that her hands stayed happy and, under Captain John Mullowney, smart. Tom had a feeling she'd provide enough action for him, to start with.

Part of this feeling stemmed from the thrill with which he looked forward to the courtesy visit he must make on Captain Mullowney when he went on board the ship. Jim had painted John Mullowney as a great man, with a name for making his converted merchantman sail and fight like a frigate. Jim also had drawn him as an unusual American. Said Jim:

"He's of Irish descent, like us. Ran away one winter night to join General George Washington at Valley Forge, arriving ragged, with his feet bleeding.

"Smallest drummer boy in the Continental Army, he faced a redcoat charge with a squad of infantry at the Battle of Monmouth the following summer. When the Americans began to retreat, our Johnny pounded out 'Yankee Doodle' on his drum so hard the troops returned to the charge—and forced the British to retreat. That won him commendation for both his energy and his bravery."

After the Revolution, said Jim, "Johnny went to sea in frigate *United States* as lieutenant. Last November he took over command of *Ganges* from Captain Thomas Tingey in the Windward Islands."

Quite a man indeed!

"Don't call him Johnny to his face," Jim had advised.

When the stage let Tom off at New Castle, where the Dutch had erected a fort in 1651 and William Penn had landed a year later en route to founding Pennsylvania, he tried to hide a creeping nervousness. The big carpet bag that held all his gear gave him something to do with at least one hand as he made his way across The Green. Beyond narrow brick houses, he saw New Castle Academy. On The Strand, he looked out over the Delaware River.

In the river, some two or three miles wide at this point, *Ganges* loomed huge with her stern gallery and high quarter-deck. Her three masts rose, in Tom's estimation, practically to the low-hanging clouds that threatened rain. With all sail set, she'd take considerable handling!

"Like her?"

Yanked out of his reverie, Tom turned to a uniformed youth his own age but heavier framed and stockier, blond hair escaping under a peaked cap.

"I'm about to sail in her," said Tom.

"You won't even get on board if we don't round up my jolly-boat crew!"

The stranger shoved out a bronzed hand, shook Tom's, and pointed to a ship's boat hauled up on the beach.

"I'm Rex Otis. The Skipper sent me ashore to pick up the mail. When I got back, every last man had vamoosed. I should have known better."

Tossing Tom's bag into the boat, Rex started up The Strand toward a weatherbeaten sign—The Brown Horse—hanging over a big doorway. Tom followed. Inside the tavern, whose oil lamps vaguely lighted a long and narrow common room, Rex Otis looked over the crowded tables and bellowed.

"Ahoy, you men off *Ganges!* Get me back on board before the Old Man swims ashore and personally claps you in irons!"

Tom watched with amusement as the midshipman's extravagant statement brought eight beer-drinking sailors to their feet, wiping mouths with thick fingers. In nondescript work clothes, they silently followed Rex and Tom to the jolly boat, launched her, and took up their oars. In the stern sheets as the craft drew alongside *Ganges* in midstream, Rex winked at Tom.

"Now you know what the mere mention of Captain John Mullowney's wrath does to brave men. Speak softly when you meet him."

Oh, oh!

Following Rex up the ship's side, Tom gave the quarterdeck his first official salute. His second went to the officer of the deck, a tall lieutenant, with:

"Midshipman Thomas Macdonough, sir, reporting for duty."

"I recognized you a hundred yards off. You're the spitting image of your brother Jim." The lieutenant turned to Rex. "Take this young gentleman into your mess, Mr. Otis. Show him where to swing his hammock."

Tom followed Rex, down a seemingly endless series of companionways and ladders that reached ever deeper into the ship's dark interior, to a dimly-lit compartment about twelve feet square. On its walls small oil flames flickered in glass chimneys.

"Welcome to Midshipmen's Country." Rex's expansive gesture took in a table, several wooden lockers, six chairs, and what looked like a sideboard. "Don't tell me you like it, because *I* don't . . . nor do the four others we berth with."

Silent, Tom tried to adjust to below decks smell and damp.

"Last man in," said Red, "acts as mess president, or caterer. Which means you keep track of our rations, supervise our messboy's cooking, swipe everything decent you can from every other mess—including the Captain's—and shoot any rats that poke their snouts through the bulkheads."

Rex rambled on.

"Any hooks that nobody else uses will hold your hammock. So you can't sling it until everyone else turns in . . . after the messboy digs one up for you." He pointed to the bulkheads. "If that green color offends you, the paint locker's just along the passageway. As mess president you have unofficial permission to lift whatever color appeals to you and repaint the entire berth—by yourself, of course."

Rex laughed heartily.

"Oh, yes, watch out for the president of the lieutenants' mess," he cautioned. "I made the mistake of substituting a pair of my stockings for a chicken he had boiling in a galley pot last week and, because my mother had broidered my initials on 'em, he knows our mess took his chicken."

Still silent, Tom tried to assess the percentage of truth in Rex's monologue.

"Cat got your tongue?"

"Just figuring," said Tom.

Rex lifted a blond eyebrow. "How to jump ship?"

Tom shook his head. "How to get invited to the Captain's mess. I want to see for myself if he serves anything worth stealing."

Rex slapped Tom's back.

"That's the spirit," he roared. "Just don't accept his invitation for a Sunday. It's his day for eating midshipmen."

"Any reason I can't make my duty call on him this afternoon?"

Rex lifted his eyebrow again.

"You're a brave man, Thomas Macdonough. Took me a

week to get up nerve to make my call, but I'll gladly lead you
to him right now."

Tom followed his guide up another series of ladders and
along passageways aft to the captain's cabin. With each step
his heart pounded harder. He wanted to make the best possible
first impression on Captain Mullowney. Maybe he shouldn't
rush this too fast. The Captain might have his mind on more
important problems. Tomorrow might . . .

Rex rapped sharply on the cabin door and, with a wave of
his hand and a look on his face that said, "We who are about
to die salute you," vanished.

Tom braced for the encounter. He took off his cap, threw
out his chest, and stood tall.

"Come in!" boomed a salty voice.

At the bidding, Tom's courage melted. St. George going to
attack the dragon could not have trembled more. Quaking,
he opened the door and stepped into the cabin.

The room seemed huge, many times as large as the midshipmen's berth. Comfortable mahogany chairs stood about.
Through glass windows in the ship's stern Tom saw the river.
At a large, polished desk, onto which daylight shone through
a side port, a figure in blue sat writing. For a small-sized man,
Captain John Mullowney seemed to pack a lot of power. Tom
could feel it across the room. "Don't call him Johnny to his
face," Jim had advised!

Cap in hand Tom crossed to the desk and waited, trying to
keep his knees from sounding like clacking castanets. After
an eternity, the Captain slowly straightened to look the new
midshipman over.

Tom saluted, and with mouth so dry he could hardly form
words said: "Midshipman Thomas Macdonough reporting, sir."

With a hand shaking like *Connie Too*'s lateen sail in a blow,
he proffered his orders from Secretary Stoddert.

Captain Mullowney merely glanced at the papers, quizzical
blue eyes scrutinizing Tom closely.

"Show those to the purser when he comes back on board next week, from Philadelphia. Meanwhile put yourself under the first lieutenant's orders."

He frowned. Suddenly:

"What do you know about the Caribbean Sea?"

Tom coughed, trying to think and, then, trying to find voice.

"Only what my brother's told me, sir. He sailed there with Captain Truxton."

As if his visitor had breathed a password, Captain Mullowney bounded out of his chair, reached across the desk, seized Tom's hand, and pulled the astounded midshipman closer.

"Well, well, well! Glad to have you on board, young man. Half the boys the Department sends me have never even smelled salt water. Truxton, eh?"

"Yes, sir." Did the Captain think *he'd* sailed with the great Truxton?

Dropping back into his chair momentarily, Captain Mullowney reached to one side of the desk and pulled a book from a bulkhead shelf.

"Here!" He rose abruptly again. "We'll probably sail to Havana and Santo Domingo. This will give you some background."

The Old Man certainly moved fast. Tom found himself outside the cabin, book in one hand and cap in the other, both palms sweating. It seemed as though he'd spent a month in the dynamic Skipper's presence, but he'd faced Captain John Mullowney for less than two minutes. In that short time he'd uttered only three short sentences and one brief, "Yes, sir."

He'd better learn to speak up or he'd never make lieutenant!

☆☆☆ CHAPTER 4

Unstrung, Tom wandered on deck with the *Naval Gazeteer,* which Captain Mullowney had thrust into his hand.

"The Caribbean Sea," he read, "stretches 1,800 miles from the Serpent's Mouth, between the Island of Tobago and South America, to Yucatan Channel, between Central America and Cuba. Four to seven hundred miles wide, it mothers the Gulf Stream."

His eyes caught colorful phrases as he leafed through the British book. "Coral atolls ... beaches fringed with coconut palms ... forests often rise sheer from the coast ... alive with frigate birds, noddies, scarlet flamingos, parrots ... giant green turtles ... flying fish ... alligators doze on bars at the entrances to the rivers."

He searched for Havana.

"Mister Macdonough!"

The bellow jerked him to attention. He gulped, saluted, and gazed into the stolid face of a very imposing officer with gold epaulet on his left shoulder.

Third Lieutenant Love looked grimmer than a schoolteacher.

Tom lifted his cap. "Yes, sir?" he offered politely.

"On deck you work the ship!" snapped the lieutenant. "Book reading you do below."

"Yes, *sir!*"

Tom closed the book, and didn't get to study it again for weeks.

Instead, he learned shipboard routine, came to recognize

officers and mates as individuals, and observed how handily *Ganges'* two-hundred-odd seamen took their big craft upriver to Philadelphia for stores and ammunition, and down again. Belowdecks he threw himself wholeheartedly into his mess caterer job and very soon got to know the other midshipmen, particularly his starboard berth companions who initiated him quickly into the life of Midshipmen's Country.

Pretending wakefulness the first night, they swung their hammocks at the last possible moment and, at first sound of the bugler's taps, doused lights—leaving Tom to grope in the dark for hooks. Before dawn next morning they shook him out of his canvas sling . . . and he found they'd tied his clothes into knots. To top things off, they'd filled his good boots with water.

Tom went quietly to work, his berthmates whistling contentedly as they dressed. Laboriously untying knots, he finally got into his clothes with a hope that they'd unwrinkle some with wearing, emptied his boots, and forced a foot into each as the quickest way to dry them. Finished, he joined the whistling—and the fraternity of United States midshipmen.

Having accepted Tom, all hands kept the starboard berth filled with noisy laughter when they came below to take their ease. Mostly they chattered about money. Always in debt apparently, midshipmen had money on their minds more than ship's chores.

As Bill Blaine—hawk-nosed, black-eyed, and thin as a lath —expounded one night:

"Cash should never be trifled with. We should pay it the courtesy of spending it for good food and drink, not waste it on local tailors and shoemakers."

Joel Calkins and Joseph Robins, who looked like a couple of pudgy brothers and answered to the same nickname Joe— to everyone's confusion—loudly confirmed Bill Blaine's fiscal philosophy. Only Chet Clark entered a demurrer. Leaning back in his chair, long-stockinged legs outstretched, he had an easy manner and a soft voice.

"Save your money the way I do, Tom," he said. "For the sunny shores of Cuba and Santo Domingo, for horseback rides and dinners with senoritas."

Tom took in every idea they threw out, amused at how young all his companions seemed as they went on to discuss shirtmakers and hatters and washerwomen. Having spent all their allowances, including advances from a soft-hearted purser, they planned to pay off their New Castle bills with a flying topsail—putting to sea without settling up.

Tom's strong sense of moral obligation kept him from going along with this method of dealing with creditors, but he had to smile at the thought of the fun he'd see the day before *Ganges* sailed, when anxious tradesmen tried to collect from his bankrupt berthmates.

In the end, ironically, Tom himself caused the greatest part of sailing day's monetary embarrassment. He didn't plan to make things more difficult. It just naturally came about.

Heading for dinner at The Brown Horse tavern two nights before putting to sea, he felt only ordinarily well. At dinner, over oysters and turkey and rum and wine, he perked up. On the roundabout way back to ship after dinner, he felt great. So did Rex, Bill, the two Joes, and Chet.

Crossing The Green, Tom found his eyes traveling to the big white Congregational Church. Slowly his gaze climbed to the steeple where a huge bronze bell hung temptingly silent. As his eyes rested on the bell, a wonderful idea flashed into his mind. Cagily, he gave the others a few seconds to ponder on what they could do with such a bell. After perfect timing, he declared:

"This seems like a mighty quiet town!"

Without breaking into the church—"we just pushed on a door, sir," Tom explained later—he and Rex climbed to the belfry, lowered the bell rope outside the steeple to eagerly waiting midshipmen, and galloped down to join in ringing out

a clamor that pulled night-capped heads to nearly every bedroom window in New Castle.

So far, so good. The starboard berth six had brought life
to the sleepy town. But the clanging ended abruptly when the
big bronze bell toppled off its supporting timbers . . . the midshipmen scattered into the night.

"You got out lucky," the first lieutenant stated flatly next
day when he summoned the guilty six to the quarter-deck and
read them a letter of outrage from the Congregational min-
ister. "That bell could have crashed through the entire church."

They'd been afraid of that.

"See the purser and collect on your wages," the lieutenant
ordered. "Mister Macdonough will take your money to the
dominie and pay all damages in full."

As Tom pointed out to the others, tongue-in-cheek:

"We could have wasted all that money on local tailors and
shoemakers!"

Preparing for sea, Tom grew very close to Rex Otis. The
stocky midshipman had a way with sailors, who perked up
whenever he appeared. Tom appreciated that this ability to
handle men would carry an officer far up the naval ladder. He
wanted to learn all he could about it.

"What makes you so popular?" he gibed.

"Mostly, the gals like the way I—"

"With seamen!"

Rex peered furtively around the deck like a spy about to sell
state secrets.

"Seriously!" said Tom.

Rex dropped his facetious manner.

"Well, I learned very early to put my dignity in my pocket,"
he said frankly. "When a lieutenant bawls me out, I bawl out
a sailor."

To Tom this seemed exactly the wrong way to go about
winning respect.

"Last voyage, the Old Man barked at me when I forgot to

lift my cap in passing him on deck," said Rex as if to prove his point. "So I turned and chewed out the nearest seaman.

" 'Why did you do that?' the Captain wanted to know.

" 'Just passing your compliment on, sir.'

"The Old Man nearly split a gut. He hasn't sworn at me since!"

Tom found Rex's weakness, too. At the rail while *Ganges* tossed at anchor in a choppy sea brought upriver by an early summer squall, Rex heaved up. Between heavings his face looked green.

"Wish I could sail as well as I can swim," he moaned. "And don't tell me the greatest navy captains get sick every time they put to sea!"

With mock tenderness, Tom placed a hand on Rex's shoulder.

"Want a nice fat piece of pork to eat?"

Rex swung a weak fist at Tom's head and hung over the rail again, groaning.

Dated 25 May, orders arrived for *Ganges* to take under convoy all merchant ships ready at New Castle and destined for Santo Domingo and Havana.

Having escorted twenty-two merchantmen north on their previous voyage, this job held no glamor for most of the ship's officers.

"You should see the way some of these merchant captains sail their ships!" Rex exclaimed. "They spread themselves all over the ocean instead of keeping in tight formation. A French privateer can slip among 'em at night and cut one out before the victim knows what's happened to him."

To Tom, however, the prospect of escorting two ships, two brigs, and two schooners to the distant Caribbean loomed as high adventure. Many of the vessels carried valuable cargoes, and Secretary Stoddert had written Captain Mullowney to "pay them all the attention in your power. If they leave you, the fault will not be yours; but do not let it be said that you neglected them."

Turning over mail for delivery to frigate *Constellation,* and orders for *Warren* to return to the United States, the Navy Secretary had wished Captain Mullowney and *Ganges* great success and glory.

The Secretary had further observed, according to the first lieutenant, "that the way to render most important services to your country, most effectually to protect its commerce, and to acquire personal honors is to keep constantly cruising—to go into port as seldom as possible."

"Which," the lieutenant added, "also keeps the crew healthy."

Completing preparations and complying with all sanitation laws, *Ganges* dropped downstream with her convoy to the capes of Delaware.

At daylight on 4 June the lieutenant called all hands to up-anchor.

The ship came alive. Within five minutes of leaving their hammocks, *Ganges'* seamen had brought the anchor up, the capstan winding in the cable until the lieutenant's command came down from the quarter-deck to pawl the heavy drum.

Assigned to the lieutenant as messenger, Tom watched.

Boatswain and mates shrilly whistled all hands to make sail.

"Aloft, sail-loosers!"

Topmen scrambled up ratlines. Seamen spread over decks to rouse the halyards and sheets which would hoist and hold out the yards.

"Trice up, lay out, and loose!"

From aloft:

"All ready on the topsail yards, all ready on the lower yards, sir."

"Let fall!"

Sails dropped from their gaskets in graceful folds . . .

hauled out to the end of the yards . . . everything went home together.

The order to hoist away topsails boomed through the lieutenant's trumpet and yards flew aloft. Topgallant sails and royals spread to the wind. In a moment, it seemed to Tom, a cloud of canvas billowed from deck to trucks. From mainmast streamed the commission pennant, long and narrow like a ribbon.

With the order to counter-brace the yards ready for casting, seamen again manned the capstan bars and hove the anchor up to the bow.

Like a dog sniffing game, *Ganges* eagerly turned her head seaward. Yards squared, lifts and trusses hauled taut, she drove before the wind. The ship looked trim, and her lieutenant appeared pleased. Captain Mullowney's face, too, carried a small smile of satisfaction.

Ganges' seamen knew their jobs. A well-trained crew, they'd performed a sailing miracle. Tom had wondered, while rigging *Constellation*'s model under his brother's critical eye, how any group of men—even the most skillful—could make all those lines and spars and sails come together in a functioning whole. Now he knew.

Past Cape Henlopen, *Ganges* rounded into the Atlantic Ocean's wind and hung, while the Delaware Bay pilot climbed down her Jacob's ladder to a small shore boat. With the dropping of the pilot, Tom felt a twinge of homesickness. Then the salt smell of open ocean flowed through him like a magic potion. To the seven seas at last!

☆☆☆ CHAPTER 5

Captain Mullowney wasted no time. He made his first day out a typical exercise day. With *Ganges'* canvas drawing full, seamen swabbed decks to a cleanliness that satisfied the lieutenant and, consequently, the Captain eating breakfast.

At 10 A.M. the marine drummer beat to quarters and Tom raced to the quarter-deck. Before the drumming stopped officers, gunners, and sailors had manned battle stations.

In absolute quiet, muster began. Officers reported on their divisions. In turn the lieutenant reported to the Captain who, sword buckled on, stood on the quarter-deck surrounded by midshipmen.

With the Captain's order to proceed with the exercise, lieutenants barked commands to each division . . . individual gun captains shouted commands to loaders, shellmen, handspikemen, tacklemen, spongers, and powdermen . . . gun crews moved fast and sure to successive "cast loose and provide," "run," "serve vent and sponge," "load," "prime," "point," "ready-fire!"

Tom knew that gunners called their "long guns" by the size of the iron ball they fired, from 1½-pounders to 42-pounders, but he'd never seen a ship's crew handle naval cannons before.

From casting loose of lanyards which enabled the first loader, aided by the first sponger, to remove the upper half of the gun port in the ship's rail and let down the lower half, each man knew his duty. As Tom watched an 18-pounder on the larboard quarter, handspikemen raised the breech of the two-ton cannon so that the second gun captain could place the quoin (wood wedge) between breech and carriage to elevate on target . . . tacklemen trained the gun sideways . . . and gun captain touched the powder-filled vent with a quick-match (a long piece of slow-burning rope) to fire the gun.

Ganges' gunners handled their 18-pounders like toys. Expert, they could fire a shot a minute . . . they could damage an enemy ship at a mile, often farther.

By moving from station to station around the gun, "with the sun," every man in a gun crew learned the duties of all the others. In an emergency, each could carry out any job.

Tom thrilled at how close gunners came to hitting lumber-and-canvas targets which, set adrift in the distance, they straddled and bracketed with their shots, adjusting sights after every splash to compensate for error.

Tom watched gunners carefully push each cartridge (powder packed in a wool bag) into the gun muzzle, seat the ball, and ram in a wad of rope yarn to keep the iron shot from rolling out as the ship rolled. Because they shot on the ship's downward roll, the balls they fired would, mostly, hull an enemy—damaging her below the waterline. Boom . . . smoke from the gun's muzzle . . . a wait as the crew watched the ball arc toward the target . . . a geyser close to the mark! Tom could see how much this accuracy pleased Captain Mullowney.

When *Ganges* fought at close range in battle, Tom learned, her gunners would seat a cylindrical canvas bag where they now seated the iron ball. This bag would hold grapeshot comprising a cluster of iron balls, or canister shot which scattered small balls the size of two or three musket balls, or shot tied together by chain, or shot with a solid iron-bar connection—to tear sails and rigging and make such a shambles above and on deck that the enemy ship could not fight her guns.

After an hour's exercising, *Ganges'* crews secured their guns and closed gun ports.

Second day of Captain Mullowney's rigorous training schedule found Tom assigned as a loader in the nine man crew of a starboard division 18-pounder. Within a week, the lieutenant named him regular gun captain.

Tom's imagination soared. At this rate he'd make lieutenant in jig time! He'd—

Rex pulled him back to earth.

"Don't let your head swell. Last trip everyone in our berth made gun captain third day out."

"You must have put to sea short-handed!"

"We did," Rex confessed.

Besides gunnery, Tom studied seamanship. Under Sailing Master Ik Williams, whose long blue coat and tricorn hat lacked only a little of a lieutenant's gold braid, he spent from eleven o'clock to noon on navigation. During this period he also skylarked with his companions.

But Ik Williams—both powerful and gentle—had years of seafaring under his belt and handled midshipmen easily.

"You just need," he told his charges at the start of their first lesson, "to have your little noses wiped on occasion, your behinds spanked now and then, and your ears warmed every so often with a kind word of the sort your mamas used to hand out when you fell down and scraped a knee."

Ik quietly instructed them in the rudiments of navigation—with books, in the lee of a jolly boat; with quadrants, on the quarter-deck. Each morning at seven bells—a half hour before twelve—he encouraged them as they tried to bring the sun's image down to the horizon with their cumbersome instruments and to figure out the ship's noon latitude.

Discovering that the ship had only two quadrants on board, the half dozen student-navigators ganged up to make out a requisition for individual equipment. Instead of getting in the way of their prank, Ik gravely told them he'd send their request to Captain Mullowney for approval. Giving them no chance to run for cover, he did just that.

The Captain promptly summoned the midshipmen to his cabin. Ik kept a straight face while they took off their caps and gingerly stepped inside where the Captain grimly ordered them to stand at rigid attention. Brow furrowed, he gave each miscreant an individual stare that sparked hot flashes. For several minutes then, he strode up and down, hands behind back, head bowed in thought. At last:

"Steward!" he shouted to his messboy.

An alert young Negro who had worked for the Mullowney family on shore entered the cabin. "Yes, Captain Mullowney?"

"Bring my best madeira!"

The Skipper's face unfroze.

"And glasses for all."

Sighs of relief bounced off the bulkheads and, in the next half hour, the captain entertained the midshipmen with stories of his own first days at sea.

"We *really* gave our Old Man trouble," he declared, "shining the sun in his eyes when he stood on the horse block trying to take noon sights. He once logged 'no observation—sun in a state of fusion.'"

The audience roared.

"He made us all use a single quadrant. But we sent in separate observed latitudes on sheets of colored paper folded into stars, squares, and cocked hats. When he ordered no more colored paper, just cartridge paper, we took him at his word —sent him regular cartridge paper two feet long and one foot wide, with every observation different!"

The midshipmen guffawed again. But in the middle of their laughter, the Captain's voice abruptly changed tone.

"I'm telling my cook to make no special dishes for your guests when we put into port, nor to lend you my decanters and dish covers when you entertain." He waved them out of the cabin.

To their backs, he called:

"That is, until every single man of you learns to shoot the sun as accurately as the Sailing Master does it."

At that moment Midshipman Macdonough began to understand why *Ganges'* seamen sailed and shot with such preci-

sion, why her officers so frequently let a sense of humor show
through their tough discipline. In Tom's eyes Captain John
Mullowney, smallest drummer boy in the Continental Army,
became a great person.

Tom enjoyed life on the ocean. Weather fine, winds light,
sea quiet . . . What pleasure cruise could bring such fresh in-
terest each new day?

On the third afternoon out, 6 June, the lookout on the foremast head shouted down from the royal yards:

"Sail ho!"

Captain Mullowney rushed from his cabin.

"Masthead, there! Where away is the sail?"

"Two points off the starboard bow, sir."

"What does she look like?"

"Like a brig, sir."

The Captain waited several minutes.

"Masthead, there! What does she look like now?"

The lookout, an old-timer with pointed gray beard, called
down:

"Like a merchantman to me, sir."

Giving chase, *Ganges* closed with brig *Huntress* within the
hour. Alongside, Captain Mullowney talked through his brass
trumpet with her captain. Out of Savannah, the brig sailed for
New York. Dipping her ensign, *Ganges* hauled hard into the
wind and rejoined the convoy whose merchantmen already
wandered over the Atlantic Ocean like playful ducklings elud-
ing an anxious mother.

On 10 June, brig *Susanna* signaled from the convoy. *Ganges*
went over, to find her skipper in his berth with fever. Surgeon's
Mate Gershom Jackways, tall and scrawny as a scarecrow,
went on board to doctor the ailing officer. Captain Mullowney
took the brig in tow. Nine days later, at half past two, in the
afternoon, *Susanna* signaled her skipper's death. Captain Mullowney sent Lieutenant Samuel Cummins with two men to
take command. The convoy moved on.

After another week of pleasant weather, the lookout on *Ganges'* mainmast head sighted a man-of-war as the sun came up. Before Captain Mullowney could get out on deck, the lieutenant with the duty ordered ship's guns manned. Tom raced to his. Port opened, cannon rolled into position ready to fire, Tom's heart pounded like a blacksmith's hammer.

His excitement quickly cooled. From the man aloft came recognition of the man-of-war.

"She's American, sir. Looks like *Constitution.*"

She closed with *Ganges* to the accompaniment of welcoming cheers from both vessels.

At half past nine in the morning, having spoken with Captain Silas Talbot, Captain Mullowney visited the handsome 44-gun frigate in a sea ceremony which to Tom seemed glamorous beyond belief.

A picked crew lowered Captain Mullowney's gig from stern davits and brought it alongside *Ganges'* starboard side. Belowdecks, in the captain's cabin, Tom heard bellowing.

"Boy, lay out my best uniform and sword. Lay out my gloves."

Boy, do this! Boy, do that! Tom smiled. Even a captain found it exciting to make a formal call on another captain!

On deck, the Old Man looked exactly as Tom felt a naval officer should look—erect, confident, as unperturbed as though minutes earlier he hadn't shouted for help in getting dressed. Three feet behind, walked the solemn first lieutenant.

Saluting the quarter-deck sharply, Captain Mullowney strode to the ship's ladder. As he passed between six sailors in glazed hats, spotless blue coats and pants, and shining boots, the boatswain piped shrilly. With impressive dignity Captain Mullowney then let himself down to a tilting stage which the boatswain's mates had rigged and, unaided, got into the gig's stern sheets.

Six erect oars lowered at the cockswain's command and sped the gig over the ocean's long swells toward *Constitution* whose 234-foot mainmast towered above landing stage, side-boys, and officers awaiting the distinguished visitor. Tom couldn't quite make out which he felt most at this thrilling moment—pride in his commander or pride in his own small role in his country's activities.

He felt the same emotion again, and as deeply, when Captain Mullowney ceremoniously returned to *Ganges*. For with him the Captain brought exciting news.

Constitution had bet a cask of Madeira on a race against a British frigate whose officers had called the American warship a "fir-built monster." Captain Mullowney glowed as he told the story.

"Begun at daybreak to continue till sunset," he reported, "the race started with a beat dead to windward. *Constitution*'s first lieutenant, Isaac Hull, kept her crew on deck . . . they took their meals on their feet. *Constitution* ate into the wind in a way to make her builder's heart feel good. By noon she'd run up a spanking lead . . . by sunset she had the Englishman hull down!"

Constitution's fame, Captain Mullowney finished, now spread around the sailing world. Tom, too, glowed.

☆☆☆ CHAPTER 6

On 27 June, *Ganges* turned four of her merchantmen over to *Constitution* for safe passage to Santo Domingo and proceeded with the two remaining vessels toward Havana via the Windward Passage that links the Atlantic with the Caribbean.

On 9 July, having rounded Cuba's western end in pleasant

weather, *Ganges* approached Morro Castle which bore ESE two leagues off at 8 A.M. At half past eleven, she exchanged gun salutes with the fort and came to in seven fathoms of water.

Tom looked forward to visiting the city. But Captain Mullowney followed Secretary Stoddert's instructions to the letter, delivered his convoy, and immediately went out on patrol. *Ganges* stayed in Havana harbor only one night.

Tom did not get on shore. Even so, he fell in love with the Caribbean from the ship's rail. Soft moonlight silvered the scene. Hills, valleys, harbor, and distant ocean spread before him in enchanting beauty. Lights from whitewashed houses reflected in smooth water beneath the ship as if in a liquid mirror. Tropic flowers drifted sweet scents through quiet air.

The cruise itself, however, presented another picture, less enchanting. Tropical sun by day burned and blistered hands and faces as *Ganges'* small-boat crews scoured Cuba's northern coast and its adjacent keys and islets.

Whether chasing a suspected vessel far to seaward or dragging a ship's boat up a narrow creek—past jutting roots or overhanging mangrove branches—or pushing as they waded a wide but shallow lagoon, the day's work proved almost unendurable. Swarms of stinging mosquitoes and pricking sand flies goaded crews almost to madness.

Whenever *Ganges* lay becalmed, the water's surface gathered a carpeting of the ship's own dust and filth for several fathoms around her hull. Untempered by wind, the sun scorched down on her deck like fire: pitch melted and ran from her seams; paint blistered on her sides. Water allowances never seemed enough; nor did rum rations.

At night the sea became brilliantly phosphorescent. Under way, *Ganges'* prow tossed waves in curls of flame. At anchor, a luminous track frequently betrayed a fleeing dolphin to a hungry shark whose rapacious rush for food would leave a sparkling wake that ended in a bright, destructive swirl.

Ganges also faced the threat of seasonal hurricanes. Accord-

ing to West Indians and the *Naval Gazeteer,* from which Tom
now and again read aloud to his berthmates, "the sky reddens
when the Carib god Huracan frowns. When he purses his lips,
clouds gather and tides rise. He blows a circular tempest."
Between late June and early November, the *Gazeteer* reported,
the Caribbean might see as many as fourteen hurricanes, each
spreading thirty miles wide with winds ranging to 200 miles
an hour.

A falling barometer usually gave warning, but not ade-
quately. And in this part of the world, old hands told Tom,
a squall that packed the punch of a small hurricane could
come up out of nowhere and knock a vessel down on its beam
ends.

When the wind freshened on the fourth night out of Havana,
Tom felt no particular apprehension. He'd taken to the variety
of ship's life like a cat to milk. In tropic dusk he watched topmen shorten sail, reefing and hoisting. Automatically his eyes
went to the ship's life raft, hung outside the larboard rail.

Invented by Captain John Barry of frigate *United States,*
it consisted of two empty quarter casks, secured together by
cross-pieces and, for easy sighting, carrying a flag on a staff.
Every American naval vessel mounted such a raft, guarded
on twenty-four-hour watch by a man with hatchet ready to
cut it clear.

Before sail-handlers could get *Ganges'* canvas lashed, the
squall struck with terrifying impact and a foremast topboy
shrieked as the ship's pitch threw him off the yard. He fell,
struck the bellied foresail, and bounced overboard.

Tom shouted—the watchman chopped his raft free. Overside too went gratings, coops, and every floatable article seamen could lay desperate hands on—to no avail!

For *Ganges,* her masts bending like wands, rushed through
the water like a panicked whale. Before the quartermaster
could get helm up, she heeled over . . . yardarms almost

touched the waves and Tom thought she'd never right herself again.

"Clue up—haul down—let fly all!" Captain Mullowney trumpeted.

Wind roared . . . foam flew over decks . . . ribboned sails flashed and flapped . . . timbers groaned.

Captain Mullowney called the carpenter and his men aft with axes.

"Stand by to cut away the mizzenmast," he ordered.

The grim carpenters grouped to chop shrouds and clear away wreckage when the mast fell . . . Captain Mullowney lifted his trumpet to pass the word. At that moment the ship lurched like a fallen horse struggling to regain its footing on an icy hill. Righting herself by degrees, *Ganges* finally answered her helm and flew before the wind.

When Tom's heart stopped pounding and he managed to loosen his vise-like grip on the shroud to which he'd clung, he heard the Deck Officer announce he could not lower a boat in existing seas to search for the lost topboy. Whereupon Captain Mullowney ordered battle lanterns lit fore and aft. Stationing lookouts aloft and along the deck, he called for complete quiet from all hands.

Ears strained for a cry; eyes searched the inky dark for a glimpse of the boy. *Ganges* stood by all night and next morning.

At noon the Captain put the ship once more on course in a confused chop with little or no wind to steady her. As she rolled, the carpenter's mates made and secured a new life raft.

Standing alongside Rex Otis with his eyes on the work party as the ship took an exceptional roll, Tom grabbed the rail. But Rex, by quixotic misfortune, stepped on a line at the exact instant that the slapping main course snapped the line out. Rex rose ten feet into the air and flew head-over-heels into the sea.

Almost before Rex struck the water, Tom cut away the

freshly constructed life raft . . . and the cry "Man overboard!" rang through the ship for a second time in less than twenty-four hours.

Eyes glued to the raft with its flag, Tom thanked heaven as Rex swam to it with strong strokes. But when Rex tried to clamber onto the raft, it turned over. Tom's heart sank . . . he lost sight of the raft in deep troughs. Then he saw Rex dive under the raft, come up between its crosspieces, and perch triumphantly on top!

From the quarter-deck Captain Mullowney watched with open admiration as Rex tamed his stubborn mount. Calling for volunteers, he sent the first cutter after the midshipman.

Tom expressed his relief at getting Rex safely off the life raft with a quip: "Don't go messing our berth with all that salt water you've soaked up."

Rex smiled expansively as the cutter's crew bent to their oars and rowed him to the ship.

"Thanks, maties," he said, with a feigned British accent.

Patrol duty held a never-ending fascination for Tom. At dawn, he had no idea what the new day would bring. For along with privateers the West Indies spawned many small, armed vessels which belonged to no state in particular. Called Picaroons, they changed their character according to the ships they fell in with. Little better than pirates, they hid out among the Caribbean's myriad islands and bays. At any time a strange sail might provide *Ganges* with a fight; it might not.

At 6 A.M., on 20 July, for example, *Ganges* went in chase of a brig to windward. When she caught up with her quarry four hours later, small boats scurried away from the brig's side. Sent from *Ganges,* Tom found her to be American brig *Dispatch,* bound for Baltimore from Gonaïves. She had fallen captive to a French privateer whose prize crew had held her eleven days. Captain Mullowney ordered her to Philadelphia, with Midshipman Howard Jones on board as prize master.

Then, on 22 July, *Ganges* sighted and recognized a French cruiser flying the tricolor. Like a good schooner, the Frenchman managed to keep her distance. But, inevitably, *Ganges* forced her to run for the safety of neutral Matanzas harbor and its fort.

While Tom figuratively bit his fingernails down to his elbows, Captain Mullowney waited off-shore for the enemy cruiser to try to slip out, perhaps for the island of Guadalupe where the French fleet maintained a base.

During the vigil, *Ganges* kept ordinarily busy: she fired a shot at a ship, which showed papers for *Penelope,* bound to Baltimore . . . she spoke ship *Washington* of Philadelphia, bound to Havana . . . and on 26 July after some lightning, a squall knocked landsman William McMuller overboard, to drown despite every effort to save him.

As if laughing at what it had done, the fitful weather again turned pleasant; pleasant enough so that, at 3 P.M. of 29 July, the French privateer hoisted her colors and put out of Matanzas.

Tom heard the lookout's warning, and his heart leaped as *Ganges* clapped on full sail and gave chase.

At battle station, Tom watched the ship drop behind the cruiser. He saw her gain for a time. Later, the wind favored the Frenchman again.

After four hours *Ganges* closed to within a half-mile, Captain Mullowney fired a 9-pounder from the bow to bring the enemy to and, when she continued to run, fired a second shot . . . and a third—dropping each ball for enough away to warn but not to injure the flying schooner. But she refused to come to; instead, she hauled her wind and ran back for shore.

Brusquely, Captain Mullowney ordered Tom's division to "fire for effect." Under no circumstances, he pronounced, must the privateer escape!

This was it!

Touching quick match to gun's primed vent, Tom saw

smoke, heard a blast, and watched an 18-pound ball hurtle toward target. His heart almost stopped as he waited. Would the ball hit the mark?

It did! The gun crew shouted. And a second ball, from another cannon, sent the Frenchman's frantic crew leaping overboard—to swim for shore regardless of sharks!

Ganges closed, her guns firing steadily. Too excited to count, Tom never knew how many shots his 18-pounder fired. He did observe, nevertheless, at action's end, that *La Fortune* rested on the beach with three men wounded on her deck. *Ganges'* work boats immediately towed the schooner off.

"We'll all share in good prize money," Rex informed the starboard berth that night.

Next day, Captain Mullowney sent Lieutenant Love, Midshipmen Elbert and Clark, and seven foremast hands on board to take the prize home to the United States for private sale.

As *Ganges* winged for Havana under blue skies, Tom relived the chase, the fight, and the capture of his first enemy ship. Captain Mullowney wrote to the Secretary of the Navy that the coast again was clear of French privateers.

☆☆☆ CHAPTER 7

Two months out from home, *Ganges* again dropped anchor abreast of Havana's Morro Castle, furled sails, sent her boatswain out ahead in a jolly boat to shout orders that squared her yards, and began a welcome stay in port.

Time: 7 P.M., 31 July.

Everything about Havana harbor excited Midshipman Thomas Macdonough. Bright Spanish colors flew over the fort. Jabbering men and women rowed crowded bumboats around the ship to offer baskets of bananas, oranges, soursops, fried flying fish, eggs, poultry, milk—delicacies to tempt men long at sea.

From *Ganges'* rail Tom also saw the lieutenant go on shore with dispatches and watched seamen scamper into lowered liberty boats. No shore leave for him, however. He had deck duty and, as the saying goes, plenty of time to ponder his sins. Chiefly, he regretted not having written the family since leaving New Castle in May. But that, he knew, followed usual naval practice. Every sailor found it hard to put a letter together . . . witness Jim's lack of news about his leg.

Black fins caught his attention, gliding around the anchored ship. Tigers of the sea, natives called these sharks. Tom shivered and Dennis Kelly, a middle-aged marine with black eyes and hair, came up just in time to pull Tom from thoughts of what would happen to a man falling overboard.

Military in bearing when on duty, off duty Kelly liked to gripe and at length. Tom often picked up useful information from Kelly's babble. So he listened.

"Think we'll ever get our prize money for capturing that Frenchman?" Kelly opened.

"Of course. Why not?"

"Because Johnny Bret's mother hasn't yet seen a penny from *Ganges'* first cruise," Kelly groused. "Us marines get the short end of the stick every time. Except Lieutenant Gale, that is." His eyes lighted.

"When Captain Richard Dale had command of *Ganges,*" he told Tom with gusto, "an officer struck Lieutenant Gale and he could get no satisfaction from either the captain or the officer. So the minute the ship arrived home, Gale called the officer out and shot him in a duel." Kelly paused for effect. "Next cruise, politeness was restored!"

Always some friction between sailors and marines. But, Tom knew, they'd fight for each other at the right time and place.

Plump but dour ship's fifer Jedidiah Allen joined his fellow marine.

"I smell yellow jack," he said, and peered overside at the sharks.

"You're out of your mind," Kelly declared.

"It smelled just like this ten years ago when we dropped anchor in Charlotte Amalie," said the fifer in a funereal voice. "A couple of dozen sharks followed our ship into the harbor. Stayed with us day and night."

He let that sink in. Then:

"I said to the Old Man 'Captain, sir, them there sharks has orders from yellow jack to guard us.' "

"What happened?"

"Half the crew come down with the yellow fever. Most of 'em died."

The melancholy fifer hurled a broken gun quoin into the water. Sharks skittered after the wood wedge, leaving a phosphorescent wake. A moment later they returned to stand guard.

As darkness fell of a sudden as it does in the tropics, without twilight, Tom's thoughts went off in many directions. He'd come far with navigation, with gunnery, and with seamanship in general—thanks to Jim's head start training. Best, he'd learned how to command. He couldn't figure exactly what had happened, but somehow he felt grown up. Not older, heaven forbid, but capable of getting along in most situations.

He didn't have Rex Otis's light touch. Instead, he had a dignity uniquely his own, that got across to his fellow midshipmen and officers and to the seamen with whom he worked. They understood that he meant what he said, would do what he said. They knew where he stood.

He could see that living in Midshipmen's Country with skylarking youths his own age, taking orders from mature officers, passing the orders on to gray-bearded seamen, and working alongside them all in hot and cold, dry and wet, had broadened his horizon considerably. He'd had a look-see at their qualities and discovered that, given the chance, they'd rather perform like heroes than villains. Not all, of course, but ninety-nine percent.

Could only three months have passed since the Navy Secretary ordered him to sea? Maturing, he'd traveled a long distance!

Tom went on shore next morning, not on liberty but in charge of the Captain's gig. His duty looked simple: to keep an eye on the boat's crew while Captain Mullowney went about official affairs in town.

Tom fully appreciated his responsibility. He intended to fulfill it. He'd see that the crew behaved, stayed alert to bring Captain Mullowney back to the ship. He wouldn't stand for any shenanigans like the mail party's at New Castle.

The trip from ship to shore went smoothly ... until, in handing Captain Mullowney from gig to dock, Tom's cap got knocked off. During the important business of landing the Captain safely, no one dared take time out to rescue the cap. It sank.

With the fierce tropic sun beating down on his uncovered head, Tom deliberated, decided, and acted fast the moment Captain Mullowney disappeared from view. He put Big Mike Dougherty in charge.

"I'll be back in ten minutes," he told the gig's party. "I'm going to buy me a hat."

To Big Mike he added, as severely as he could:

"If a single man leaves this spot I'll have you and him court-martialed!"

"Aye, aye, sir."

The group saluted, very respectfully.

Three blocks along the waterfront, Tom found a shop with

out-door displays of clothing that included straw hats. In front of a counter full of native weaves stood a broad-chested, thin-hipped American naval lieutenant. His exuberance intrigued Tom. Setting a light straw rakishly on his jet-black hair, the lieutenant gave a violent shake to test the hat for size, and passed Tom a friendly wink.

"How does it look?"

"So good," said Tom, "I think I'll buy me one like it."

He tried the nearest on for size.

"I just lost my cap," he said, and dug into his pants pocket for money.

"A native straw's better than your Navy cap anyway," the lieutenant said. "The all-around brim keeps sun out of your eyes and off the back of your neck."

He turned to the shop's smiling proprietor and spoke rapid Spanish. He turned back to Tom. "This fellow wants a dollar for your hat, but fifty cents'll give him twice the profit he deserves. Don't pay more."

Tom handed over fifty cents.

"Thanks for your help," he told the lieutenant. "I'm Thomas Macdonough, ship *Ganges.*"

"Glad to know you. My name's Stephen Decatur, brig *Norfolk.* Ever try one of these?"

He offered Tom a short tube of tobacco rolled in a leaf.

"They tell me Columbus found the natives smoking seegars like this in 1492," he said.

Tom touched the tobacco roll to the lieutenant's already lighted tube, drew his breath in—and coughed out a white smoke cloud that filled his eyes with tears.

"Hang loose, son," said Decatur. "You'll get used to 'em."

By the time Tom recovered, *Norfolk*'s handsome lieutenant had ambled off.

Straw hat plopped casually on his head, Tom strode toward Captain Mullowney's gig. Stimulated by the enjoyable encounter and puffing on the gift seegar, he felt a terrible panic as he neared the boat. How had he dared turn his back on land-starved sailors!

Heart in mouth, he reached the gig. Every man stood at attention, with a coconut in hand. They'd waited dutifully! Dougherty saluted easily. Tom's heart fell back into normal position.

"Will you join us in drinking coconut milk, sir?" Big Mike asked.

"Thank you," said Tom. "I'm parched."

From a pile in the gig's bow Doughtery selected a particularly large coconut, punched out two holes in its top with his marlinspike, and politely handed the nut to Tom. Tom drank off the refreshing milk, and felt better. That seegar of Decatur's had made him mighty groggy!

"Delicious! I feel better already."

Time passed pleasantly in the shade of a low coral wall. The gig's oarsmen sat quietly and drank from more coconuts while Tom, shaded by his new straw hat, patiently awaited the captain. Gradually, however, so imperceptibly that Tom didn't realize until too late, the scene changed.

The men began to sing ... a light hum at first, soon reaching a raucous chorus ... until they sounded exactly like any roistering songsters in any waterfront tavern. At that moment, Captain Mullowney appeared.

Tom jumped to his feet. "Atten-tion!"

Instead of springing up at sight of their commander, the gig's oarsmen genially lifted their coconuts like champagne glasses in a formal toast. After that, with guilty grins, they tried to push to their feet. By holding onto the wall with one hand as if countering a roily sea, half the group succeeded in standing.

Captain Mullowney's blue eyes searched Tom's face.

"I find these men drunk, Mister Macdonough!"

Tom's jaw dropped. Of course they were drunk! But how? "They just sat by the wall drinking coconut milk," he babbled. "I thought there could be no objection to that, sir. It was very hot."

Captain Mullowney momentarily turned his head. When he had himself under control, he asked:

"Have you ever heard, Mister Macdonough, of 'sucking the monkey'?"

"No, sir."

"When you pour the milk out of a coconut," said the Captain, "and substitute rum for the milk and sell the coconut to a sailor he 'sucks the monkey.' The coconut the men gave *you* hadn't been monkeyed with!"

Captain Mullowney added:

"I'll take my lunch on shore. Have the men and the gig ready for me at four o'clock."

Left in the middle of an awkward salute, Tom let his mind gallop over ways and means to sober up the gig's crew. Which of the seamen had deliberately knocked his cap off to start this, anyway?

☆☆☆ CHAPTER 8

At 5 A.M., on 3 August, *Ganges* sailed out of Havana harbor on Midshipman Thomas Macdonough's second patrol.

Action built up slowly. On 4 August, *Ganges* spoke 36-gun British warship *Apollo,* Captain Ellicott. Two days later she stopped American brig *Hope,* Captain Edmonds, bound from Jamaica to Philadelphia. On 9 August, she went after a schooner.

From the start of this pursuit Tom smelled trouble. Between noon and one, when *Ganges* drew close enough to fire her 9-pounder and bring the schooner into the wind, his feeling built into a premonition of danger.

Rowed toward the schooner, to board with Lieutenant Love, he passed under her stern and read her name—*Phoebe.* Zero Coffin's slave ship!

Boarding, Tom kept an eye out for the schooner's bearded mate while he listened to Captain Pardon Bennet make no bones about discussing his cargo of "black ivory" with the lieutenant. *Phoebe,* he admitted callously, had left the coast of Africa thirty-eight days earlier with three hundred men and women chained belowdecks. The slave trader regretted only that *Ganges* had caught him.

When Tom went below to inspect, the slaves numbered only one hundred and twenty. In their filthy prison, more than half had died from lack of water, lack of food, lack of air! Tom shivered at the thought.

He shivered again, and looked up. Glowering in the companionway as though Tom personally had blasted his hopes for a quick fortune, stood *Phoebe*'s mate. In the instant Tom's eyes fell on him, Zero flung a horn-handled knife at Tom's chest.

Tom twisted, instinctively raising his right arm in protection, and the flying knife scraped his chest—to cut through his hand and thus pin his arm to the bulkhead. Blood flowed down the wood wall. A second knife raised, Zero rushed at him with blazing eyes.

Tom kicked twice at Zero's groin, though he knew he couldn't stop Zero and his stored-up hatred for long. Tom's third kick never reached its mark. Because, as his boot lashed out, a shot rang down the companionway.

Sinking to his knees, Zero toppled sideways with a look of amazement on his face. The knife slid from his fingers. From what seemed miles away Lieutenant Love's voice reached Tom's ears.

"I always wondered if these Navy pistols could kill a man."

From start to finish, the action had lasted less than a minute—not the lifetime Tom had lived through!

On 11 August, under the fort at Matanzas, at half past three in the afternoon, Midshipman Macdonough's dreams of Caribbean glory ended.

In its most virulent form, yellow jack struck.

Ganges' sick bay—and makeshift hospital facilities in every available space—quickly filled with men rent by parching thirst, partial suffocation, convulsive spasms.

Fifer Allen had called yellow jack "a devil incarnate." First came a slight headache, then vomiting, then insensibility. As the fifer so funereally had said, "You can take your rum allowance in the morning and find yourself dead as a herring afore night!"

Dr. Jackways did his best, but couldn't beat this devil. At 6 A.M., 17 August, Captain Mullowney headed for the hospitals of Havana.

Abreast of Morro Castle next day, *Ganges* anchored beside *Warren* which already had lost forty men and officers to yellow jack. *Ganges* proceeded to do the same.

Tom's first touch of headache came the morning of 19 August. On a stretcher, vomiting, he found a sick detail rowing him ashore two hours later along with Rex Otis, Bill Blaine, two other midshipmen, and Dr. Jackways himself. In a following boat came Dennis Kelly, Fifer Jedidiah Allen, a third marine, and three seamen, including Big Mike Dougherty.

Anxious to get out of danger fast, the sick detail drove their infected shipmates in horse-drawn carts to a foul Spanish hospital—and wished them luck.

Fighting yellow fever proved gruesome. All around him, Tom saw bloodshot eyes and heard maniacal laughing. He watched brave men, pushed past human endurance, die, saw the bodies summarily carted away for burial.

He never knew how long he lay, unconscious and untended, in a corner of the stinking pesthouse, holding stubbornly to life. Nor did he ever learn which courageous Cuban attendant fanned the dying spark of his existence back into an ever-warmer ember. When, finally, his mind began to clear, he could think only of how often Dr. Jackways had called the West Indies—with their fevers and other climatic diseases—"just hospitals to die in."

The Surgeon's Mate also had said that men with spare frames stood a better chance to survive the West Indies than did fleshy men. Apparently he had the right of it—two-thirds of the right at least. For the scarecrow doctor got out of the hospital alive with Tom at the end of the battle with yellow jack, along with Rex Otis, who was reduced to a scant hundred pounds.

The emaciated trio found themselves on the street in white hospital pants and jacket and canvas shoes, destitute. Their uniforms had gone into the hospital's fires, burned—only known way to contain yellow fever's spread. Mysteriously, Tom's straw hat eluded the flames. He hadn't asked how; he just clapped it on his head and stumbled with his shipmates to the American consulate.

Because *Ganges* had sailed back to the United States while they fought yellow fever, Consul John Morton gave them enough clothes to get them home and paid their passage on a merchantman belonging to a Philadelphia shipping firm.

Misfortune still pursued. Huracan frowned, pursed his lips, and blew a circular tempest under a red sky.

The storm hit the homebound merchantman with a one hundred-knot force, tossing the vessel like a board, straining her masts, and ripping storm staysails from boltropes. Walls opened with every roll. Seamen manned pumps for hours on end. No one slept. Tom could hear surf pounding downwind.

The captain's problem: whether to lie-to in an effort to ride the hurricane out . . . or attempt to wear ship, get her around on the other tack, and try to claw off dangerous lee shoals.

When the captain gave his order to wear, seamen stood ready to cut away rigging if a mast fell. Axe in hand, Tom joined them. Groggily, the water-logged ship yielded to the helm. And then, as Tom watched, a gigantic wave toppled over the bulwarks and swamped the deck. What an end to his brief career!

Tom and the seamen raised their axes . . . but they held their blows. The ship slowly fell off . . . limped away from the pounding surf.

For forty-eight hours Tom, Rex, and Dr. Jackways had no food. All fires doused, the ship's cook had not cooked. And when a calmer ocean at last made it possible to prepare a hot meal, an English warship threw a warning shot over the merchantman's bow and seized the vessel, for carrying Spanish property in her hold.

The warship's considerate captain did, however, transfer the three starved Americans to a nearby American brig which he had just searched and given permission to proceed. So that, at last, Tom raced toward Norfolk and home, as though, Dr. Jackways declared, "the girls on shore had a towrope secured to the ship and hauled us with a speed proportioned to their impatience."

A light fog lifted as the brig reached beautiful Chesapeake Bay. And Tom never tasted a better supper—oysters and sausage—than the trio ate in Glen's Hotel. Nor did he ever sleep sounder than he did that night in one of the ten beds in room No. 2 on the top floor.

After goodbys to Rex and the Surgeon's Mate, he took two days to reach home. On the first, he found a sloop to ferry him across the bay to its eastern shore. On the second, Thanksgiving eve, he stepped off the stage in front of The Trap's general store.

On the far side of the road he glimpsed curious faces peering out of the Macdonough parlor window. But no one there recognized, in this thin and haggard figure with canvas shoes on its feet and beat-up straw hat on its head, the spruce midshipman they'd so proudly sent off to sea last May.

As the stage drove away, however, Tom's heart surged with happiness. The door of the house flew open, shrieks of joy greeted him, and his brothers and sisters raced across the road.

Hester flung herself into his arms.

"Oh, Tom!" she cried. "We thought you were dead!"

PART 2
In the Blue
Mediterranean

Atlantic Ocean

SPAIN

Corsica

ITALY

Malaga Valencia

Palma

Sardinia

Naples

Strait of Gibralter

MEDITERRANEAN SEA

Sicily Syracuse

Crete

Algiers Tunis

MOROCCO

ALGERIA

TUNISIA

TRIPOLITANIA

Tripoli

1802-1803

U. S. S. CONSTELLATION

☆☆☆ CHAPTER 9

Two months after Midshipman Thomas Macdonough reached home to enjoy his loving family and to recuperate from his battle with yellow fever, France decided to pull her fleet out of the West Indies. She made peace with the United States, 1 February 1801.

Thomas Jefferson's just elected administration took over in March and new Navy Secretary Robert Smith immediately:

Called all ships home from the Caribbean . . .

Put *Ganges* on a Philadelphia auction block and sold her . . .

Dismissed practically all naval officers . . .

Left Midshipman Macdonough high and dry on the beach. Tom's blood boiled.

The Navy had just begun to show the world how her young officers could protect their country and their country's commerce. Why cast them off now?

"Before I even made lieutenant!"

Irate, he went into action.

He rode first to Cool Spring, Wilmington home of state congressman Caesar Augustus Rodney who had sponsored him for his midshipman's warrant. In a panelled library, painted the softest shade of blue he'd ever laid eyes on, he sat in a leather-covered wing chair and poured his feelings into the receptive ear of his family's old friend.

57

Caesar Rodney listened gravely to the full recital. From a handsome mahogany box atop the even handsomer mahogany desk at which he sat, the congressman then took two seegars. Tom smiled inwardly, recalled the seegar he'd smoked with Stephen Decatur, and accepted one.

Lighting Tom's with a twist of paper first held in a fireplace flame, Mr. Rodney quietly said:

"I appreciate how much the Navy means to you, Tom. And I've kept abreast of the decommissioning you got caught in . . . 'sails lowered, colors displayed, a mourning salute of thirteen guns . . . men shouldering their sea bags and walking off like Ulysses with his oar.' But I happen also to know that Mr. Jefferson wants Navy Secretary Smith to start putting young men of flexible minds into our frigates, all thirteen of which we've kept."

Young men . . . flexible minds . . . this sounded promising! Before Tom could evaluate the news, Mr. Rodney asked:

"How much do you know about the Barbary states?"

The abrupt question made Tom blink. But he quickly assembled the few facts he'd picked up—from newspaper reading and from conversations on ship and on shore with British and Spanish officers.

"I know their names, sir. Morocco, Algiers, Tunis, Tripoli. I know they lie along the Mediterranean coast of North Africa. And that they raid our shipping."

"They exact tribute from *every* ship that sails into the Mediterranean," Caesar Rodney declared. "They commit out-and-out piracy!"

His mouth thinned into a straight line, his hands clenched. Obviously he felt strongly on the subject and intended his original question only to set the stage so that he could express his emotions to an understanding audience. Which he proceeded to do.

"Before the Revolutionary War," he told Tom, "England's navy protected our eighty or hundred ships that sailed to the

Mediterranean each year with meat, fish, and other articles. From Virginia and the Carolinas and Massachusetts, these vessels carried British colonial immunity. After the Revolution, however, we no longer held that immunity. Right away, an Algerine cruiser captured American brig *Maria,* out of Boston, and sold her crew into slavery!"

Caesar Rodney paused to see if Tom appreciated the full import of the word slavery.

"Did you know," he went on, coldly calm now, "that on Thanksgiving Day eight years ago every church on the New England seaboard took up collections to ransom fellow townsmen in ten captured American vessels?"

Tom winced. This indeed hit where it hurt.

"Did you also know that when Mr. Jefferson lived in France as American ambassador and wanted his young daughter to visit him there, he directed her to sail in a French or English vessel having a Mediterranean pass issued by the pirates? He didn't trust her to an American ship."

From his desk, Mr. Rodney picked up a paper.

"Mr. Jefferson used to get bills like this from the pirates for sailors they'd captured when they plundered our ships."

Tom read the copy of one such bill:

3 captains	@	$6,000 each	$18,000.
2 mates	@	4,000	8,000.
2 passengers	@	4,000	8,000.
14 seamen	@	1,400	19,600.
			53,600.
	Customary 11% bonus		5,896.
	TOTAL		$59,496.
	for 21 persons		

"Who got the bonus?" Tom asked, amazed.

"The pirate ambassador!"

Mr. Rodney continued indignant.

"When Mr. Jefferson went from Paris to London in 1786 to meet the Tripoline ambassador, he found that a treaty with Tripoli would cost $150,000—plus another $15,000 for the ambassador."

Well launched on his subject, Caesar Rodney pictured conditions that kept Tom's blood hot.

"For three hundred years," he said, "the four Barbary states have proved themselves ferocious barbarians. One of their chiefs took delight in jumping on his horse, scimitar in hand, and lopping off the head of the groom who held the bridle!"

Mr. Rodney puffed his seegar, silent for several minutes. Then:

"England could have suppressed this deliberate policy of piracy," he went on, still angry. "But, as Benjamin Franklin reported when he went to France as American ambassador, London merchants said that if there were no pirates in the Mediterranean it would be worth England's while to train some. Lord Sheffield told Parliament only six years ago that England has the power to suppress piracy but doesn't. Because, if she did, the little countries in the Mediterranean would get more of the shipping trade."

After another minute of irate puffing, Caesar Rodney continued:

"The pirates don't want peace, either. As the Dey of Algiers puts it, 'What would I do with my corsairs if I make peace with everybody? My soldiers can't live on their miserable allowances.' "

Mr. Rodney laughed wryly.

"So the nations buy immunity. We bought it from Morocco in 1786, from Algiers in 1795, from Tripoli a year later, and from Tunis a year after that."

Mr. Rodney stood up.

"The kow-towing we've done, too! Why, we even made a present to the Dey of Algiers of a 36-gun frigate—*Crescent*, built in Portsmouth, New Hampshire. We loaded it with naval stores worth $100,000 and added twenty-six barrels full of silver dollars. Can you guess what that was for?"

He stopped pacing long enough to glare at Tom.

"That was for being late in fulfilling our treaty obligations. And do you know *when* that was? Just two years ago!"

After more pacing:

"When General William Eaton, our consul in Algiers, went to talk to the Dey about it, he found him in a small dimly-lit room with narrow windows protected by iron bars. He described him as 'a huge, shaggy beast, seated like a bear on his hind legs and grinning.' "

The indignant patriot shook his head, as if unable to believe such proceedings possible.

"Just last year, when Captain Bainbridge in frigate *George Washington* went to pay our annual tribute, the Dey ordered him to run an errand to Constantinople—*flying the Algerine flag!* The Dey told Bainbridge that because we pay him tribute, we become his slaves!"

Caesar Rodney obviously had suffered deeply under these humiliations to his country.

"When we gave that frigate *Crescent* to the Dey of Algiers, the Bashaw of Tripoli got excited. He sent word to President Adams that he wanted a frigate too, and wanted it quick! After that, the Bey of Tunis complained that some of the tribute planks and oars we sent him were too short!"

Caesar Rodney threw up his hands in disgust. With an effort he calmed himself again and sat down.

"As you will recall, Tom, Congress intended to stop all this nonsense back in 1794 and authorized construction of six big frigates—*Constitution, Constellation, Congress, Chesapeake, President,* and *United States.* But when the four Barbary states conveniently decided they'd sign treaties if we paid them for keeping the peace, we stopped work on the frigates, until the recent hostilities with France."

Mr. Rodney's expression lightened a little.

"Well," he said, "now that Mr. Jefferson's President, he'll get Congress's back up again. He's not going to declare war outright against the Barbary pirates, but he's going to send Captain Richard Dale to the Mediterranean with a fleet."

Tom stiffened at this announcement.

"I'm glad you feel about this as I do, Tom, because I think the Navy will need you," said his host. "We can't go on paying tribute to barbarians who won't honor treaties, can we?"

☆☆☆ CHAPTER 10

Tom returned to The Trap from Cool Spring buoyant, optimistic.

"I'm going to Washington and talk with the new Secretary of the Navy," he told his family. "He needs some nimble brains and sea experience."

Hester shrieked excitedly from the kitchen.

"Take me with you, Tom? Please! I'd love to see Congress House and the President's Mansion. Everyone says they're simply wonderful."

The Washington trip panned out well. Hester found all the sights of the ten-year-old "city in the woods" wonderful indeed. And Tom, having located the Navy Department which only recently had moved its staff of seventeen from Philadelphia, found the Navy Secretary accessible.

Sitting up smartly across the mahogany desk from dour but informal Robert Smith, who leaned back in his brass-studded leather chair, Tom stated his case simply and directly. He told what he'd done so far at sea, expressed his desire to do a good deal more, and explained why. The Secretary listened with attentive ear.

His response came loud, clear, and in the identical words Jim had used earlier: "You'll do."

Walking Tom to the door of an anteroom, the Secretary turned him over to his assistant, Charles Washington Goldsborough.

"We will continue Mister Macdonough in the service," he announced, "available for duty in the Mediterranean."

Only after Tom had left the building and begun to tell Hester what had happened did he realize that he'd made his appeal to the Secretary entirely on his own merits. He'd forgotten to present the letter Caesar Rodney had given him to use as an introduction!

As before, Tom waited for orders to go to sea, this time with less impatience. Now he appreciated how much Jim and Hester and Sam and Jane and little Johnny and Joe meant to him as his family; he might not write them often—or at all!— but he certainly loved them. For Jane, who insisted on sewing him a new wardrobe to replace the uniforms burned in the Havana hospital, he had a special affection.

While he stood by, word reached the United States that Tripoli had declared war. Lieutenant Andrew Sterett, in 12-gun schooner *Enterprise,* had fought and captured 14-gun ship-of-war *Tripoli* in a three-hour battle that left the pirate vessel a shambles.

"The Navy will not start a war—only Congress can do that," Caesar Rodney had said. "But if any pirate state declares war *on us,* the Navy will strike at once!"

Tom's waiting ended in October, after a long and happy summer. His orders put him on board *Constellation,* refitting at Philadelphia.

When frigate *Constellation* first put to sea 23 June 1798 under a beautiful fifteen-starred and fifteen-striped flag—

national symbol that included Vermont and Kentucky with the original thirteen states—Captain Thomas Truxton had told his ship's company:

"We have an infant Navy to foster."

He had proceeded forthwith to forge United States naval tradition on the new frigate with his own spirit, skill, and discipline.

Riding to Philadelphia to board her, Tom's excitement grew with every passing milestone. His mind ranged over details of her sail plan—which he'd learned so thoroughly by rigging and re-rigging her model—and of her construction, which he'd learned from Jim and from newspaper accounts.

The Treasury Department had bought materials for hull and spars. Naval Agents, who for their work received two and half percent on approved bills, contracted for labor and bought less important materials. The shipbuilders—Samuel and Joseph Sterrett and their supervisor David Stodder—had responsibility for workmen, for materials used, and for following Joshua Humphreys' plans.

Nautical experts had praised her as one of those happy products never afterward surpassed.

"In the beauty of her hull," said one, "she is unequalled by anything I have seen afloat. The easy swell and curvature of her sides and the general harmony of her proportions are inimitable."

Good men had helped put her together, including Paul Revere, whose copper sheathing guarded her hull against worms and whose copper bolts held her timbers fast.

For the Navy, Captain Truxton had watched over *Constellation*'s birth—superintending her construction and fitting out. And he found, on her first cruise, that she worked at her seams—as many critics of Humphreys' radical designs had predicted.

Returning her to dry dock, Truxton replaced some of her guns with lighter pieces, put back to sea, stood up against everything that wind and water could pit against her, and fought *L'Insurgente* with such power that critics changed their tune. To the Secretary of the Navy, Truxton wrote:

I have seen so much in the public Prints of the Sailing of Barry's ship [frigate *United States*] and so much more bombastical Nonsense of that at Boston [*Constitution*] that I am at a loss to make a Report, with Respect to the Sailing of this Frigate on that Score, with any Degree of Satisfaction to myself.

I shall therefore only say that in no Instance of Chace during our Cruise, was half our Canvass necessary to overhaul the fastest sailing vessel we met, some of which were termed before Flyers. Should we therefore meet the *United States* and *Constitution,* you need not be surprised if you hear, that in going by and large, she outsails them both.

And she is the easiest Ship I ever was in.

As newspapers reported, *Constellation* had indeed proven fastest frigate on the seas, her 14-knot top speed under Truxton beating Barry's 13½ with *United States* and Nicholson's and Hull's 13½ with *Constitution.*

But victories in the Caribbean over *L'Insurgente* and 52-gun *Vengeance* had taken considerable out of her: she'd lost her foremast in the first battle; she'd limped into Jamaica after the second, not a spar or fathom of rigging abaft the foremast.

West Indies weather treated her harshly, too, particularly one gale that had hit her the previous January. Of this gale, her present commander, Alexander Murray, a hard-of-hearing Marylander who had started as a lieutenant in the Revolutionary Army and changed over to the Navy on frigate *Trumbull,* had reported:

Top-gallant yards and mast taken down ... scudding under a reefed foresail (only sail we could set) ... lee sheet gave way and brought us by the lee. One sea making a perfect breach over us, stove in all ports and in a few minutes we had near 6 feet water in the hold, the most of which entered our hatchways before we could get them properly secured.

Began to cut away mizzenmast lee shrouds and stays and some of the weather ones, when we succeeded in getting aft the lee fore tacks and a preventer sheet, which played her off before the wind. We ceased cutting away. Got preventer tackles upon the mast to save it and got down the gaff, but not till it gave a crack that gave us great alarm, yet finally we secured it.

Pumps gained but little on the water in the hold and we contemplated throwing overboard our spar deck guns, but after great exertions we brought the pumps to suck, in the course of which time I was 18 hours on the deck without rest, as were the greater part of the crew—continually expected to be obliged to cut away the masts.

The next day we made sail under close reeft main and fore topsails, till by degrees we had a return of moderate weather.

In Philadelphia now for reconditioning, *Constellation* awaited Midshipman Thomas Macdonough.

☆☆☆ CHAPTER 11

Joining *Constellation* shaped up like home-coming, for the first voice Tom heard when he started up the gangway trumpeted into his ear from Rex Otis.

"Welcome aboard, Commodore!"

Tom ignored the greeting, kept a straight face as he saluted the quarter-deck, and reported in. The lieutenant on watch glanced at Tom's orders, consulted a list of names on a paper in his hand, and nodded.

"If Mister Otis will do us the honor to stow the Captain's trumpet," the lieutenant said flatly, "I will relieve him of his deck duties so that he can stage your reunion in more appropriate surroundings—the steerage."

Rex replaced the brass megaphone, saluted sharply, and lifted Tom's big carpetbag as he had that afternoon the pair first met on The Strand in New Castle. Just as he'd thrown the bag into the jolly boat then, he now tossed it unceremoniously down an open companionway. Tom knew he was home again!

Midshipman Macdonough worked hard during the next four-and-a-half months with officers and men who overhauled *Constellation* so thoroughly that he found ample opportunity to appreciate the strength and beauty builders and architects had bestowed on her.

Like other American frigates, *Constellation* carried food and water enough for a six-months' cruise with upward of three hundred and fifty officers and men, depending on many conditions. One hundred and sixty-four feet long, with displacement of 1,276 tons, her lowest guns—on the gun deck—stood eight feet above the water. This enabled her to engage triple-deck ships-of-war in heavy weather when bigger vessels would have to close their lower-deck gun ports to avoid being swamped.

Her spar deck extended from stem to stern, without a raised forecastle or poop. Her bulwarks or rails rose to a height of almost six feet, to protect men working on deck from the wind and, in battle, to shield gunners of the spar-deck's batteries.

Constellation's tall masts truly scraped the clouds, her mainmast reaching 199 feet toward the sky. Her main yardarm, which held her largest sail, the main course, extended 84 feet acrossdecks, more than twice her beam of 40 feet 6 inches.

Captain Truxton had created her sail plan. He gave her a course on foremast, mainmast, and mizzenmast, then topsail, then topgallant, and finally royal. As the sea saying went:

When freshly blow the northern gales,
Then under courses snug we fly:
When lighter breezes swell the sails,
Then royals proudly sweep the sky.

But *Constellation* also could raise skysails above her royals, add studding sails to broaden the reach of her regular sails, and set staysails between masts. Forward, she flew jib and flying jib, and below her bowsprit could carry spritsail course and spritsail topsail. Her mizzenmast held a big fore-and-aft sail called the spanker, and to this her seamen could attach a ringtail. Tom recognized her sail plan from Jim's tutelage.

Her deck layout, however, provided many variations from that of *Ganges* and he set about learning that thoroughly.

Amidships on the spar deck, midway between foremast and mainmast, lay the booms which held a 36-foot longboat, or pinnace—along with spare lumber and spars. Abaft the booms and forward of the mainmast he found gangways.

Between gangways and stern lay the quarter-deck, its starboard side reserved for Captain Murray when the frigate lay at anchor; at sea, the windward or high side belonged to the Skipper, and the lieutenants kept to leeward. When a sailor crossed the quarter-deck, he removed his hat; an officer coming on, or leaving, this place of honor, saluted.

On the quarter-deck, forward of the mizzenmast, stood a double steering helm—two spoked wheels on a drum—on which two or more men, depending on weather, swung on the spokes. Close to the steering helm, on a wood pedestal, a brass binnacle held the frigate's compass and an oil lamp "to shew the compass at night."

On davits along either quarter, hung a whaleboat. Abreast of each stood a platform covered with a wood grating—the horse-block—on which the lieutenant stood for a clear view when conning (guiding) the ship. Often—and especially during battle—a midshipman carried a portable binnacle and compass so that the officer could work the ship. The captain's gig swung over her stern.

Bulwarks around the quarter-deck and the forecastle had troughs or nettings, in which all hammocks—neatly rolled and secured with seven turns of a lashing—lay neatly packed. In heavy weather a black canvas tarpaulin covered the nettings; in good weather the spotless white hammocks lay open to sun and salt air. Hatches led from quarter-deck to officers' quarters below.

Here, on the gun deck, crew lived forward, warrant officers amidships, midshipmen and lieutenants farther aft, and Captain in the stern. The larboard side, between cabin and mainmast, served as promenade and reading room for officers.

Starboard, tucked between guns that fringed the entire deck on both sides, were schoolroom, barber shop, cobbler shop, lathe for carpenter, and cooper's workshop. Except for the schoolroom, screened by canvas, all other spaces opened onto the deck—for quick removal when gunners manned their guns. Only Captain Murray slept on the gun deck.

All others slept a deck below, the berth deck. If you measured less than five feet tall, Tom found, you could stand erect on the berth deck; for comfort, you sat.

In ten little staterooms, divided equally larboard and starboard, senior officers had their quarters. Each room held cot, bureau, and locker. Light came from outside through glass portholes, usually closed when at sea. Lieutenants had their rooms on the starboard side; opposite, lived sailing master, purser, surgeon, chaplain, and marine officer.

Open dining space, the wardroom, ran between the rooms. Here, with a skylight to give a little illumination and ventilation, the officers sat.

Midshipmen swung their hammocks in the steerage. Their messroom, one of two small rooms on either side of steerage, had a modicum of light from glass portholes which, with the ship in port, they kept open as much as possible for ventilation.

Beyond steerage and abreast of the mainmast slept the four warrant officers—boatswain, gunner, sailmaker, carpenter—each with his own room. Sick bay filled much of the bow.

Between warrant officers and sick bay—about half the frigate's length—some 300-odd crew swung their hammocks, with spreaders or sticks at each end to keep the sides apart. Thus a seaman could turn over in the hammock, lie on one side, lie on his back, even stretch out his legs—in eighteen inches of space!

Everyone washed as best he could in fresh water allotted for bathing and, weather permitting, in a bucket of salt water on deck. He relieved himself in the ship's head, a grating at her bow.

Below the waterline lived and slept the surgeon's assistants, schoolmaster, purser's assistant, and captain's clerk.

Through the cockpit, where the surgeon would operate during battle, work parties passed several times a day to the bread room and the spirits room, for ship's biscuit and for the whiskey and rum used in grog. To prevent explosion, work parties doused lights when opening the spirits room—often leaving it open all day to air. When this happened, cockpit occupants ate their meals in the dark!

The magazine abaft the bread room held barrels of gunpowder, piled from deck to overhead. And forward of the cockpit, the main hold carried provisions, paint, tar, line, and stores of every kind.

Beyond, nestled in the curving bow timbers, the purser, the boatswain, the quartermaster, the carpenter, and the gunner had storerooms. Each rated a yeoman who fitted up this tiny space according to his talent, with lines coiled, decks spotless, brasswork shining.

The gun deck saw most of each day's hour-by-hour living. Amidships, just forward of the main hatch under the booms, stood the grog tub. With highly polished brass hoops, and smelling of its rum or whiskey, this great cask held the half-spirits, half-water ration issued daily to the crew. Another cask, the scuttle butt, held drinking water; when at sea, a marine with musket and bayonet guarded this precious supply.

One of the ship's most important areas lay forward of a large hatch leading down to the crew's berth-deck quarters— the galley. Like the ship's sleeping quarters, this kitchen area had special provision for officers and for seamen. Its big wood-burning stove held three forward sections: one, on which the Captain's cook prepared his meals; a second, on which another cooked for the lieutenants; a third, on which cooks prepared the food for other officers. On the stove's after section, the coppers, "Cookie" cooked the crew's food.

Sailor diet included boiled chunks of salt beef or pork, potatoes, peas, and rice. Officers augmented these staples with special supplies that included live chickens, pigs, and other livestock crated or tethered on the gun deck between cannons.

Warm and cozy, the galley range drew the crew for smoking, gossiping, and the spinning of yarns. Here *Constellation*'s blue-jackets dried their clothes, smoked clay pipes, and told interminable stories that almost always began with "One morning in May . . ."

☆☆☆ CHAPTER 12

Refitted, *Constellation* met with cold and wet weather while shipping her crew, put fifty seamen on the sick list, and lost two. Dropping downriver over the bar, she anchored off New Castle.

Weather continued bad, winds reaching gale force, and on 6 March 1802, she parted her best bower cable, with difficulty bringing up with her sheet anchor. She had small expectation of getting a replacement for the lost 4,500-pound anchor, but her officers continued to hope the gale would abate and permit shallops to come alongside and discharge stores which the purser had managed to get down from Philadelphia.

When finally she rode quietly at a third anchor—after losing a second in the same gale—Rex Otis brought all new midshipmen an invitation to dine with Captain Murray. Now began the serious business of becoming a naval officer. What had gone before in *Ganges* served, in Tom's mind, only as preliminary training.

Captain Alexander Murray had quarters in two cabins and two staterooms. His after cabin—fifteen feet broad athwartships and seven feet fore-and-aft—was fitted with table, chairs, writing desk, lockers. In the recesses between cannons, the young dinner guests saw couches and growing plants. India matting covered the deck underfoot. Oil lamps swung from gimbals. Additional light and ventilation came through square ports with glazed windows, fitted into the stern.

Each stateroom contained a bunk, dresser, and small wardrobe. Outboard, a curved projection called the quarter-gallery held a tin tub, wash basin, and toilet facilities.

Captain Murray greeted his midshipmen in the forward cabin, which stretched the ship's full width. Chairs surrounded an extension table almost as long as the room itself; on the table a beautiful linen cloth, silverware, silver candlesticks, and glass decanters gave off a friendly aura. Two red-hot cannon balls, fitted on small iron stands, eased the cabin's damp chill.

Captain's reception-and-dining-room in port, this cabin served Sailing Master Richard Brandt at sea. Here the navigator spread his charts and instruments, and plotted the ship's position, three times a day. As in the after cabin, 24-pounders stood on each side. In battle, gunners would remove bulkheads, clear away furniture, and prepare the cannons for action.

Over a preliminary glass of Madeira, served by two messboys, Tom got his first truly close and personal glimpse of Alexander Murray. Physically, the Captain had a typical seafaring aspect. Long hair curved over his ears; a big nose separated weather-beaten cheeks. He carried himself easily. Though he wore his handsome double-epauletted uniform casually, he could, Tom saw, stand the most thorough inspection. Every gold button and every piece of gold braid lay exactly in place.

The Captain talked lightly and appeared very genial. But, because First Lieutenant Charles Stewart had not come to dine with the group, Tom had a hunch that the Old Man wanted to say things that he could more easily voice without the inhibiting presence of his senior assistant.

Following delicious boiled chicken and rice, with a fabulous apple pie, coffee, and seegars, Captain Murray rose and Tom sat up in his chair.

"I know you young gentlemen have heard all manner of rumors during the long months we've refitted our ship," Alexander Murray began in a wearisome monotone, voice of the hard-of-hearing. "Let me set you straight about our forthcoming cruise."

He made a slight pause, to draw full attention.

"We sail immediately as part of a squadron under Commodore Richard V. Morris, to relieve Commodore Dale, now protecting American commerce in the Mediterranean. We'll join flagship *Chesapeake* over there."

Pleased to see eager anticipation in the midshipmen's faces, he went on.

"Schooner *Enterprise* will follow us, and one way and another we'll meet frigates *New York, Philadelphia, George Washington,* and *Essex,* along with corvettes *Adams, John Adams,* and *Boston.*"

Captain Murray made no mention of how Thomas Truxton, in line for command of the new squadron, had resigned from the Navy rather than act as captain in his own flagship.

"Now hear this," said Captain Murray, looking severely down the dinner table, "and hear it well!"

The midshipmen stiffened.

"I will countenance no dueling in this ship."

To Tom's mind came many stories of officers shooting each other on shore and, often, on board their ships. He personally had no truck with the practice. He felt it belonged to the past. Captain Murray, relighting his seegar with a candle's flame, obviously thought so too.

"Now," the Captain went on pleasantly, "I wish you prosperity and honor. This, I hope, you will gain from attention to duty, fondness for the ship, and regard for the interests of the Navy."

Tom remembered Jim saying the same thing—Captain Truxton's words.

"First," Captain Murray told his guests, "your duty is to support the Constitution under which we derive our commissions. Second, you will perform your duty without offering an opinion, unless asked, and carry your duty out with civility and politeness to everyone. You must never lose sight of the humanity and care due your fellow officers and your men."

Captain Murray took a sip of Madeira while these points sank in, then amplified:

"No officer must ever sleep out of the ship, or permit anyone else to do so, without leave from me. Also, the officer on duty must inform me of any impropriety committed, no matter by whom. Last, officers on duty will simply lift their hat in my presence."

The Captain coughed slightly, puffed at his seegar to bring it to full fire, and looked the group over with a paternal smile.

"You will care well for your men, see that each understands his duties, exact instant obedience, superintend everything," he summed up.

Tom wondered whether the Old Man realized that he had midshipmen, not senior officers, for audience. Midshipmen didn't give orders; they just passed them on or carried them out!

"Hear this, too!" The Captain let his weather-beaten face uncrease slightly. "When I invite any of you young gentlemen to my table I expect you to set aside your duty and throw off a little of your restraint. I want to judge your capabilities. I can do that best in cheerful and convivial company."

With the creases back in his serious face, he finished:

"I don't mean to imply that a convivial guest becomes a drunkard. Any officer who does, will not remain an officer with me!"

Well—Tom told himself when finally he crawled into his larboard-berth hammock after an hour spent untying work clothes which starboard-berth pranksters had leisurely knotted and soaked in water—life goes on, even in a frigate.

"I thought we'd finished with horseplay, in *Ganges*," he observed, aloud. "But I guess some people never learn when it's time to quit."

"How about waiting an hour or so," Rex Otis suggested, "and then greasing the deck of their berth so they can't stand up when they roll out of their hammocks in the morning?"

Tom groaned.

"Haven't *you* learned either?"

☆☆☆ CHAPTER 13

Constellation's Atlantic crossing to the Rock of Gibraltar shook up, as well as shook down, officers and men alike.

Dropping Cape Henlopen on the Delaware coast at 5 P.M., Monday 15 March, Captain Murray sensed seamanship growing slacker with each nautical mile sailed. When, therefore, a week out from land, the carpenter reported a water cask leaking, Captain Murray seized the opportunity to bear down. He ordered the entire ship's company cut, from ten, to four-and-a-half pints of water daily for each man's drinking, shaving, washing.

When seamen grumbled and some muttered mutiny, he paraded the marines—about forty, under Captain James McKnight and Lieutenant Edward Hall—on the quarter-deck, muskets loaded. With all hands piped to the ship's waist, he read them the articles of war and added a few appropriate remarks to the effect that he'd flogged no man since he took over command but wouldn't flinch from it. A marine with cutlass would stand guard over the water cask with orders to split the skull of the first man that took more than his share.

"Go to quarters," he barked.

That ended that.

Three weeks later, with orders executed on the run and good spirit prevailing, Captain Murray quietly increased the water ration to normal, and every hand on board knew that he sailed under a real man.

Constellation had pleasant weather for the most part, as she sailed generally south-south-west. She spoke two brigs the first week out and supplied a barrel of beef and two of bread to the first, bound from Hamburg to New York. In these encounters, Tom took great pleasure watching *Constellation*'s seamen work their ship.

It required ninety men in each watch to handle sail on forecastle and at foremast and mainmast, not counting mizzentopmen and afterguard. In the frigate's first storm, he gaped at the number of hands needed to help wear ship—even with only fore and main topsails, and those close-reefed!

Handling yards called for brute force which the seamen supplied so readily that yards moved like toys.

After a day of fresh gales and squally weather, Tuesday 23 March, *Constellation* furled her mainsail and set the main staysail, and her lieutenants employed the frigate's people about necessary jobs.

Tom supervised the filling of four rounds of cartridges for the great guns. By this time he knew that *Constellation* still followed the gun plan set by Captain Truxton, after the frigate's shakedown cruise had shown that she carried too heavy armament.

Her gun deck had three divisions: first division, five guns and opposite, superintended by the first lieutenant; second division, five guns and opposite, superintended by the second lieutenant; third division, four guns and opposite, superintended by the third lieutenant. The three divisions totaled twenty-eight long iron 24-pounders, each weighing nearly three tons and served by ten men.

Her spar deck carried twelve long 12-pounders, with four 3-pound howitzers placed to do most good lobbing shells into an enemy. Gun captain on one of the 12-pounders, Tom enjoyed ten consecutive days in which the frigate concentrated on exercising all her guns.

Following target practice on Wednesday 7 April, Captain Murray ordered the guns sealed and assembled the crew. He felt bad, he told them, that Marine Sergeant Kinsinger and three privates had blown themselves up due to carelessness while filling musket cartridges the day before. He felt good, however, about the skill and marksmanship shown in the exercises.

"Remember," he said, "I expect you to fire fast, and every shot hit its mark."

He finished grimly:

"And you must be able to whip a Turk with a cutlass!"

Already Tom had seen, among *Constellation*'s stores, some three hundred cutlasses, axes, and pikes, along with one hundred and fifty muskets and one hundred pairs of pistols—for use when boarding an enemy.

None of the marines burned in the explosion of *Constellation*'s musket cartridges died, but each week saw one or more of the ship's company "depart this life," as Tom recorded it in his log. The deaths and burial of drummer Samuel Monroe and seaman Mathew Westman on the same day impressed him particularly. They died of natural causes, but to Tom it seemed somewhat unjust that they should go without having lifted a hand for their country except to beat on a drum or haul on a halyard. They hadn't even seen a pirate!

Sailmaker Thomas Crippen sewed drummer and seaman into their own canvas hammocks, with two cannonballs at their feet, and Tom wondered as he saw the bodies laid on a grating in the lee gangway whether the sailmaker had followed the old custom of putting his last stitch through the dead man's nose.

Ship's business delayed the funeral until after sundown.

Dark then set in, with a reefed topsail breeze. The officer on duty sent down the topgallant yards. Signal lanterns along the hammock railings faintly lighted the assembled company —some on the booms, others in the boats. Sailors in the main rigging leaned against the wind.

In oilskins, like most of the company, Captain Murray kept one eye on sails in the squall that swept the ship as he began the ceremony. Rain wilted the pages of his prayer book and the roar of wind in rigging almost drowned out his prayer. "We commit these bodies to the deep." Seamen tilted the grating, slipped off the flag which covered the sewn hammocks, and slid the white shrouds into the ocean. "Amen!"

It took Midshipman Henry Little's musical ability to dissipate Tom's gloom as he and his berthmates went below after this. But Happy Hank, on a battered guitar, beat out song after song, starting with "The hollow oak, it is his home . . . his heritage is the sea . . ." When messboy Black Peter joined the singing with a mellow plantation baritone, the entire berth fell into merrier mood. Within the hour, a messenger from the first lieutenant came below to pipe them down.

Almost before the larboard berth quieted, however, the starboard midshipmen launched an uproar. As nearly as Tom could make out when he and Rex reached the scene, Bob Adams and Bill Jennings—both short, stocky, and belligerent —had finally built a personality clash into a feud.

Adams had sounded off against Captain Murray's edict forbidding duels. Waxing louder, he'd declared he could not respect a man who'd neither fought a duel nor wanted to. At which point Jennings had shied a biscuit at his head and told him to stow the oration. In Adams's estimation, the hurled biscuit called for blood. He'd called for it "here and now."

Like Captain Murray, Tom scorned dueling. Thinking of himself as a simple country boy, he looked on the fashion of fighting with pistols over fancied slights as a barbarous way to settle arguments.

"If you can't iron out a grievance with words," he'd declared at least twice to his own mess, "then use your fists."

Now, to Bob Adams, he sounded so emphatic that he forced himself to relax immediately with:

"You don't feel the bullet that kills you, but a bloody nose hurts!"

Tom and Rex left the starboard berth members to finish calming the pair and turned in before a second messenger from on high delivered a second demand for silence in the steerage.

It took a lot to quiet these youngsters, and duty officers tried different ways every day. Tom experienced them all.

For moving on an errand too slowly, he found himself mastheaded—sent up the mainmast for the remainder of a cold, wet watch. For not touching his cap when entering Captain's Country, he rode the mizzenstay. When he omitted to address the second lieutenant with a respectful "sir," he had to stand beside the horse-block with a 24-pound shot in his hands.

Trying to steal a nap while on the quarter-deck, he waked one evening when the duty officer whacked him with a handspike. This he then had to hold, as a badge of disgrace, until he could discover another sleeper.

Better than flogging, as Tom admitted, punishments of this sort kept *Constellation*'s midshipmen and sailors in line.

With variable winds, the frigate made slow progress. But in several gales she showed that her latest alterations—including more stone ballast in her bottom—had improved her in stiffness and in sailing. Sighting the shores of Europe on 23 April, she coasted southward toward the Strait of Gilbraltar —with Captain Murray paying personal attention to "helm, log, lead, and lookout."

Platforms extended fore and aft on either side of the ship, abreast the foremast and the mizzenmast; called channels or chains, they held each mast's heavy rope-cable shrouds. Here the leadsman stood, taking soundings. Swinging a line with lead weight over his head and letting it fall a hundred feet beyond the bow, he hauled in the slack and read the depth in fathoms as marked on the line by knots and strips of leather.

Once each watch, a man in the chains determined the frigate's speed with a chip of wood bridled to a slender line knotted at certain equal distances. When he dropped the chip into the water, the quartermaster, on deck, started a half-minute sand glass. The knotted line unreeled through the seaman's fingers as the ship moved ahead of the chip, which stayed in one spot. When the sand in the top of the glass had run into the bottom, the quartermaster called "mark" ... the number of knots that had passed through the fingers of the man in the chains indicated the ship's speed in "knots."

On Thursday 29 April, *Constellation* carried away her main topgallant yard. By the time the duty officer sent up another and had the sail bent and set, the lookout spotted Apes Hill, site of the ancient Pillars of Hercules, on the north coast of Africa. Apes Hill bore SSE, distance nine miles. Six and a half weeks from Cape Henlopen!

During the excitement of sighting the Mediterranean's entrance from the ship's bow, Tom glimpsed movement on the spritsail yard under the bow. He came to sudden attention. For Bob Adams and Bill Jennings, loaded pistols in hand, had crawled to the yard's ends. Straddling the spar, they faced each other, with raised weapons.

Before the judge could give his signal to fire, Tom slipped between the knightheads and ran out on the bowsprit. In line of their fire, he dragged Bill Jennings onto the forecastle. And when Bob Adams, irate over having his surreptitious duel interrupted, followed to protest, Tom reacted strongly. He knocked their heads together. Country up-bringing lent power to his feelings and muscles. Tearful with indignation, Adams challenged him to a duel on the spot. So Tom took away the boy's pistol and shoved him aft to cool off . . .

If news of the abortive duel reached Captain Murray's ear, no word sifted down to the midshipmen's berths. And when Tom that night returned Bob's pistol and said he regretted having had to stop the fight so violently, Bob grinned sheepishly.

"Bill and I've fixed things up," he said, pointing to a blackened eye. "We're friends." He added: "Thanks, Commodore."

At 4 A.M., Friday, the Rock of Gibraltar bore NxE at two leagues, with a strong current setting east. A great day for everyone, because Davy Jones, first assistant to King Neptune, had come on board through the frigate's larboard hawse and notified Captain Murray of Neptune's intent to intiate all those who had not before passed through the Strait.

The ceremony turned out rough and raucous. Said King Neptune to Captain Murray in greeting:

"I have prepared a busy day to make your landlubbers fit subjects of my great sea domain."

When Captain Murray begged him to be as lenient as possible, Neptune responded that he'd be as severe as he could.

Primarily a crew's party, the affair provided the full treatment for midshipmen and seamen making their first Gibraltar passage. They got a good wetting in a canvas tank rigged on deck and filled with sea water, they had their heads shaved, and they had their bottoms smacked with a rope's end.

For his personal indignities, Tom received a decorated certificate signed and sealed by Captain Murray and addressed to:

"All Mermaids, Sea Serpents, Whales, Sharks, Porpoises, Dolphins, Skates, Eels, Suckers, Lobsters, Crabs, Pollywogs, and other living things of the sea." It testified that Midshipman Thomas Macdonough . . . "found worthy to be numbered as one of our truest shellbacks, has been gathered to our fold and duly initiated into the solemn mysteries of the ancient order of the deep."

After which ceremony, Her Highness Amphitrite—a goodlooking seaman in long robes and yellow rope hair—departed with King Neptune, the Royal Scribe, the Royal Doctor, the Devil, Judges, and Police.

While the new shellbacks nursed their bruises, *Constellation* beat through the Strait into the blue Mediterranean.

☆☆☆ CHAPTER 14

Midshipman Thomas Macdonough sailed into the Mediterranean Sea with anticipation tinged by misgiving.

From where he stood at *Constellation*'s starboard rail, looking half a dozen miles south across the strait, the Barbary coast stretched 2,000 miles to Egypt. From the Atlantic Ocean to Cape Bon in Tunis, the land rose quickly into mountains that reached craggy heights. Strong currents swept the coast; terrific storms often lashed it from all directions. As old-timers said, "Mediterranean winters are bleak and wet. Summers you fry in the heat!"

Scuttle butt had the frigate traveling on a fool's errand. Who expects us to put down piracy that's scourged the Mediterranean for three centuries? Even if we crush Algiers, won't Morocco, Tunis, and Tripoli keep right on seizing our merchantmen and making slaves of their crews? Doesn't Europe look at America's efforts with amusement?

Bearded seamen of long experience shook their heads when they asked these questions and finished with a grim statement of fact: "If we ever clear the pirates from the Med, we still have to make the British leave us alone everywhere else!"

Tom recalled stories he'd heard in the Caribbean, about British officers boarding American merchant vessels and taking off seamen they believed to be British even when the men claimed American citizenship. "In the Med," he'd heard, "they really act like lords of creation!"

Tom watched Captain Murray train his spyglass on the Bay of Gibraltar, some half dozen miles to the north. The roadstead looked wind-whipped and wild. Captain Murray apparently had some doubts about making his way into it.

Passing the Rock of Gibraltar to larboard, Tom watched *Constellation*'s signalmen talk with an 80-gun British man-of-war, *Caesar*—to learn that no part of the American squadron lay in the bay. Nor had Commodore Morris arrived with *Chesapeake*. This made Captain Murray senior officer on the Mediterranean station.

Not surprised then, Tom heard *Constellation*'s lieutenant order the quartermaster to steer a course for Malaga, farther along the vine-clad Spanish coast whose Moorish towers perched like sentinels on rugged promontories.

In Malaga roads lay two ships whose distinguishing American colors looked good to *Constellation*'s crew—frigates *Essex,* Captain Bainbridge, and *Philadelphia,* Captain Barron. Their loud welcoming hails rang across the roads as *Constellation* rounded to in thirteen fathoms of water.

Much happened during Tom's first days in Europe.

Given a boat to take ashore with water casks for filling,

he spent his first hour turning down spurious excuses of his land-starved seamen for going on the wharf.

"I have to buy a pair of shoes, sir" . . . One sailor, almost as young as Tom, said he'd promised to meet his wife on the pier. "There she is, sir," he pointed. Tom looked at the distant woman—at least seventy years old!

Seaman Francis Curtis succeeded in deserting. Which misfortune Tom reported to the duty officer and found he must repair. Two days' search of every dive in Malaga failed, however, to locate the deserter, and Captain Murray held Tom responsible for the sailor's defection. Tom smarted under the Captain's rebuke for dereliction of duty.

But he worked as hard as everyone else when *Constellation* left Gibraltar at half past noon on Tuesday 4 May with *Essex* and *Philadelphia* in company. The first lieutenant, observing that the other frigates forged ahead, discovered that *Constellation* drew too much water forward. A spare anchor brought on board from *Philadelphia,* Tom figured, had helped put her down by the head. With ballast shifted—a tedious, backbreaking job—she regained her speed.

The three frigates made and took in small sails occasionally, and next day at 4 P.M. again came abreast of the Rock. At 6 P.M., *Constellation* fired fifteen guns to salute Admiral Lord Keith and when at 8 P.M. she anchored in Gibraltar Bay in twenty fathoms of water, Captain Murray went on shore, seemingly pleased with the pomp and circumstance attendant upon visiting a British port.

During the next week, all hands fitted *Constellation* for patrol duty. Admiral Keith sent the frigate another anchor, with cable one hundred and one fathoms long and circumference of nineteen inches. Carpenters put a bulkhead around her forecastle, for protection against lashing gales. Lieutenants exercised her topgallant yards. Midshipman Michael B. Carroll joined her.

When His Britannic Majesty's ship *Isis* arrived with His

Royal Highness the Duke of Clarence, the American frigate took time out from sea preparations to salute the duke with twenty-one guns. Much visiting followed among senior officers of both ships, along with a contretemps one afternoon that chilled young Midshipman Macdonough who had the duty as Captain Murray's messenger.

Tom knew that at Malaga some of *Constellation*'s seamen had brought on board a Britisher who'd tired of fighting the French on a British ship-of-the-line. They hoped to get him to the United States.

But a visiting British officer had recognized the deserter. And when an officious lieutenant appeared on board *Constellation* with a formal demand for the sailor, Captain Murray had to accede to the demand. Tom took the bad news to Lieutenant Stewart who had the duty. Lieutenant Stewart called the sailor to the quarter-deck and, in front of Tom, explained to the man what had happened. He then sent the man below for his seabag.

Tom saw that Lieutenant Stewart felt as unhappy in the situation as did he. All the unfortunate seaman wanted was a chance to live free of nautical slavery. Tom appreciated that Captain Murray could do nothing to help, nor could the lieutenant, nor could he. But the sailor himself could act, and did.

He returned without his seabag. Instead, in his right hand he carried his left hand—chopped off at the wrist with an axe from the carpenter's bench below! Throwing the hand at the British lieutenant's feet, he glared straight into the officer's white face.

"I'll cut off a foot, too," he declared. "before I ever serve on another British ship!"

Constellation went into action on Tuesday 12 May, moving out of Gibraltar Bay and heading east for Algiers.

As she approached the Algerine coast, winds dropped. On Sunday 16 May, after mustering the crew for divine service, the duty officer sent the watch out in the ship's boats to tow the frigate. The boats got her onto the other tack, and at half past five Monday morning the town of Algiers bore SxE. At half past ten, *Constellation* fired a gun, at eleven she hoisted her colors and, shortly afterward, Consul Richard O'Brien came on board.

Around the Bay of Algiers Tom saw what seemed like two cities. One ran along the shore; the other lay above it, on a bluff. With fortifications and a mole, the city of Algiers comprised—he read in the *Naval Gazeteer*—some 20,000 houses with 160 mosques and 250 public baths.

"You'll get to see the town one day," Lieutenant Stewart told him, "but I doubt if you'll like it. The women go outdoors with only their eyes showing, and the men sit in coffee houses chewing opium. The city holds six thousand Christians as slaves."

White slaves in Africa!

"These Turks are an ignorant lot," said the lieutenant. "Some of their provincial governors can't even write their names."

"Do you mean Algerines when you say Turks?" Tom asked.

The lieutenant laughed. "We call 'em all Turks," he said, "because the Sultan of Turkey dominates the whole Barbary coast."

Lieutenant Stewart went on:

"We've run onto Algerine pirates sailing as far from home as Barbados in those xebecs you see in the harbor there, with three masts and long overhanging bow and stern. These Turks know how to navigate but," he laughed again, "they can't read. That's been our best protection so far against their piracy."

The lieutenant related how British cargo vessels carried ornate certificates when trading in the Mediterranean, the protection which the American colonies also had enjoyed until the Revolution.

"Now," Lieutenant Stewart told Tom, "more than one

Yankee skipper forges his own passport, knowing that the Turks can't read English. They identify the certificates by size and shape, and by the curlicues on the ornamental border."

Tom laughed at the picture.

"You should hear an American captain describe a pirate captain coming on board, looking very solemn as he pretends to read the fake documents," said Lieutenant Stewart. "First he measures to see if the paper's the right size. Then he pulls a notched stick out of a fold of his robe and puts it against the border, to see if the curlicues match the notches!"

"What if the passport doesn't fool him?"

Lieutenant Stewart left Tom at the rail to answer his own question.

Word eventually sifted down from Consul O'Brien and Captain Murray that although twelve Algerine cruisers had sailed out in the past months and had captured Spanish, Portuguese, and Genoese vessels, they had not bothered American merchantmen. The situation under control, *Constellation* moved on toward Tunis.

Whereupon word passed to the midshipmen's berths that *Constellation* carried a valuable present of arms for the Bey of Tunis. Intended to bring his country to friendly terms with the United States—terms like those supposedly existing at this time between America and Morocco and Algiers—the arms had considerable value. One musket alone had cost almost $3,500.

Because of head winds, however, *Constellation* sailed north across the Mediterranean to the Balearic Islands. At beautiful Majorca, Lieutenant Stewart went on shore to pick up a pilot who knew the Barbary coast. And not until 6 A.M. on Friday 28 May, wind NNE, did the frigate come to in six fathoms in the Bay of Tunis on Africa's north coast where American merchantman *Morning Star*, Captain Coffin, lay peacefully at anchor.

General William Eaton, American consul, came on board to lunch with Captain Murray, dine, and—with several of the frigate's officers, and with Midshipman Macdonough in charge of the gig—go on shore in the evening at the ruins of ancient Carthage. Two days later, while crew kept busy painting *Constellation*'s sides, Captain Murray, his officers, and General Eaton took America's tribute of arms to the Bey of Tunis.

"Our magnificent gift had an excellent effect," Second Lieutenant Richard Lawson later reported with considerable sarcasm, having watched his country pay tribute to a pirate nation. "The Bey seemed well disposed to show the utmost civility."

Acting Lieutenant Michael Carroll, also with considerable feeling, added optimistically, "The Old Man told us on the way back that he thinks it will not be amiss—I quote him— to show those folks our ships now and then."

Captain Murray showed the citizens of Tunis more than ships. He had *Constellation*'s crew exercise her great guns for the Bey and for all his people to see and hear. Eyes glinting, the Captain described the guns to his quarter-deck officers as "powerful advocates in our favor."

Having accomplished *Constellation*'s mission to Tunis and now receiving word from General Eaton that a Tripoline galley had gone out into the Mediterranean—"which hath created great alarm"—Captain Murray took advantage of the arrival of U.S. schooner *Enterprise* to move on Tripoli.

A year earlier, *Enterprise* had captured pirate ship-of-war *Tripoli*. Small compared with *Constellation*—eighty-four feet long—she carried seventy officers and men and twelve 6-pounders under Lieutenant Andrew Sterett. She had cost Congress $16,000 to build in 1799 for action in shoal waters. She could chase pirate gunboats wherever they chose to try to escape; modeled on the handy lines of fast Baltimore clippers, she could elude heavier vessels, too.

Now began the serious business for which President Jefferson had sent the American fleet into the Mediterranean. Tom's heart picked up its beat.

Sending *Enterprise* to Barcelona with *Morning Star* in convoy and with orders to pick up and protect any other American vessels bound out the Strait of Gibraltar, Captain Murray on 4 June pointed *Constellation* eastward—toward the city of Tripoli.

☆☆☆ CHAPTER 15

Patrol of the Barbary coast, Tom soon discovered, brought to *Constellation* the same daily chores that patrol along the coast of Cuba had brought to *Ganges*—taking off sail, putting on sail, painting, repairing, mustering for Sunday service, eating, sleeping.

Dawn came, afternoon went, evening and night passed. Weather varied from good to bad. Officers sometimes passed a compliment, more often administered a rebuke. Men worked willingly one hour, sullenly the next. Life's little events strung themselves endlessly together—but no pirates brought the action *Constellation* sought.

Coasting from Tunis, in the heart of green fields, to Tripoli, the frigate passed islands of great beauty—Pantelleria, Jerba . . . lush with corn, grapes, olives, apricots, figs, almonds—and sighted a Danish frigate. Nearing Tripoli, she spoke two Swedish frigates.

"But nary a Turk," moaned Rex Otis.

Off Tripoli *Constellation* found U.S. corvette *Boston*, Captain Daniel McNeill, and went on tame patrols with her. After a week of this, Captain Murray signaled Captain McNeill that the frigate would leave the corvette to patrol alone and would proceed to Malta or Syracuse for a supply of water.

Three days later, having skirted the island of Goza, northwest of Malta, and Cape Passero at the southeastern tip of Sicily, *Constellation* sighted Cape Murror di Porco and came to in the Bay of Syracuse with her small bower. Hoisting out the boats, Lieutenant Stewart moored the ship with the stream anchor to windward and immediately employed her carpenters in caulking the ship's seams.

After Captain Murray went on shore next morning, work parties took the frigate's water casks into the boats for filling. It would require most of the coming week to put 26,000 gallons on board.

Straw hat protecting him from the copper-colored sun's rays, Tom took in the charms of Syracuse—deep-blue sea, old breakwaters, white houses that peeped through bronzed vines. Much early Greek atmosphere remained in this city, and he could imagine ancient fleets in the quiet roadstead, anchored while commanders consulted the oracle known as the Ear of Dionysius.

On shore with Rex, he visited the vast catacombs that held the ancient dead. On horses the pair rode to the city's outskirts, and looked north to the Strait of Messina and the toe of Italy's boot.

The only real excitement of the visit came to Tom by hearsay—Lieutenant Richard Lawson, dueling with Marine Captain James McKnight, shot and killed his opponent. Outraged, Captain Murray restricted Lawson to his cabin under arrest, ordered him shipped home on the first American warship returning to the United States, and sternly suggested that friends of the dead marine put up a gravestone reading:

"He fell a victim to a false idea of honor."

Constellation's patrol off Tripoli grew ever more monotonous. Sailmakers recut sails. Carpenters built a new boat. The ship's people washed their clothes. Tom Macdonough joined his berthmates in grousing. And a Swedish admiral came on board.

Following this visit, things picked up a little. *Constellation* sailed along the Tripoline coast in company with Swedish warship *Thetis.* They spoke French brig *Du Charme,* bound to Marseille. They saw Tripoline gunboats on shore. They chased a Ragusan brig bound to Leghorn.

Action loomed when a Tripoline boat came alongside under flag of truce. But she only sought permission for a vessel with Grecian nationals on board to pass out of Tripoli under Ottoman colors. At 6 A.M. on Tuesday 20 July, *Thetis* quietly escorted the vessel out of the bay.

But twenty-four hours later the Swedish warship returned with news. The Greek captain had seen two native galleys slip into Tripoli harbor the day before. Sometime earlier these galleys had captured American brig *Franklin;* they had just brought nine of her crew as prisoners to the Bashaw of Tripoli.

First-hand details of this piracy reached *Constellation*'s company after dark that same night. Two American seamen from captured *Franklin* hailed the frigate from a small boat they rowed together, each at an oar. Barely strong enough to climb the built-in iron ladder on *Constellation*'s starboard side, they stumbled to Captain Murray's cabin. With two other midshipmen, Tom heard their pitiful story.

Burned almost as black as an Arab, the young spokesman for the tattered pair looked about Tom's age. Beneath his torn rags sores and scabs covered his stomach, back, arms, and legs. He appeared to combine in one emaciated body a wide range of diseases from boils, blotches, smallpox, and dysentery to ulcers and leprosy. The old man looked even worse.

Brig *Franklin* belonged to Philadelphia owners. Bound out of Marseille, 8 June, for the West Indies with assorted cargo, she had met three Tripoline corsairs mounting four carriage and four swivel guns.

"About a hundred pirates boarded us," the young man said, "all armed with scimitars and pistols and pikes and spears. They yelled in half-a-dozen languages. They threatened to massacre us."

The older man mumbled in his beard. It sounded to Tom as though he said, "I wish they'd of killed me."

"They broke open trunks and chests and plundered everything belowdecks," said the young seaman. "They stripped all the clothes off our backs ceptin' only our shirt and a pair of drawers. After that, they took us to Algiers and sold all but nine to the Algerines for slaves."

Tom's stomach turned over. Algiers supposedly had a peace treaty with the United States!

"They put us in a prison with a hollow square about a hundred-and-fifty feet long and three stories high," the scurfy youth went on. "We found other Americans mixed in with about six hundred of all nationalities. Daytimes the Turks loaded them with twenty-five to forty pounds of chains fastened to their waist and to a ring around their ankle and made them go out and work—I don't know what at. Us, we kept busy killin' bugs that swarmed all over our bodies!"

Captain Murray looked as though he wanted to get the pair scrubbed as fast as possible, but he listened attentively, cupping his ear so as not to miss a word.

"The stories I heard!" The sailor bit his lip as if to regain control of himself. "Americans, slaves, lying down in the street and putting their master's foot on their neck to show they're slaves. Forced to creep in the dirt and lick the dust. Fed a few ounces of stinkin' meat, a few rotten dates ... kept in cells with rattan branches for beds. And if they try to escape and get caught ... well, I don't ever want to see the way those savages run an iron-tipped pole up a man's backbone until it comes out at his shoulders ... while a band plays execution music!"

The old man looked at Captain Murray with hungry, beseeching eyes.

"We got away last night when our guards got drunk, Captain, sir," said the younger. "We stole the boat that we came out to you in. Don't let 'em take us back," he pleaded.

Tom's fists clenched; his blood ran hot. Couldn't the United States do something about this? Tripoli had declared war a year ago. Why didn't *Constellation* blast the living daylights out of the city and send the marines in to rescue every Christian slave from the Bashaw's prisons?

Next day, he found out why.

☆☆☆ CHAPTER 16

At 9 A.M. 22 July, *Constellation*'s lookout spotted a fleet of enemy gunboats some three miles to leeward of the city. Through their glasses, Captain Murray and Lieutenant Stewart counted nine sail. They made out an admiral's galley, full of men, mounting a long, brass 24-pounder, and flying a crimson flag with crescent and star.

Tom's heart pounded as Captain Murray ordered all sail and the watch crowded on every bit of canvas the frigate would carry. He never spent a more exciting day.

On *Constellation*'s spar deck, he stood at his gun while Captain Murray set out to cut the Tripoline gunboats off before they could beach under the city's forts.

At eleven, the frigate came within gunshot of the fleeing boats. At half past eleven, Tom brought his 12-pounder to bear on the pirates. His target—the admiral's galley.

Constellation also had come within reach of shore batteries, and for a few minutes it looked as though Captain Murray intended to stand out to sea. But when the batteries began to fire on the frigate, the Captain went in to attack the gunboats which now had six thousand soldiers of the Bashaw's army drawn up to protect them. Rounding to in twelve fathoms of water—her pilot much alarmed over standing in so near the land—*Constellation* became the target of both forts and galleys.

In the Caribbean, *Ganges* had done the shooting—at ships that did not shoot back. Now Tom faced both land and naval guns; pirate batteries and boats proceeded to give him his baptism of fire. As Captain Murray had ordered, he kept his 12-pounder hot.

Tom now got an understanding of the problem the Navy faced in dealing with Tripoli. For, much as Captain Murray would have liked to go right up to the forts and reduce them with *Constellation*'s carronades, a vessel of her draft could not effectively bombard the city. Rocks and reefs made a near approach foolhardy, even with a local pilot.

Should the frigate succeed in closing on the forts, light Tripoline war vessels and gunboats, concealed in bays and inlets along the indented coast, would fall on her . . . and while these small craft harassed her, the city's powerful forts would batter the frigate to pieces.

How, then, to subdue the pirates of the Barbary coast? As Shakespeare put it, that was the question—and a mighty tough one, Tom finally realized. Three American presidents already had tried to cope with it. So had one American commodore, Richard Dale. But beyond paying wasted tribute to the Emperor of Morocco, the Dey of Algiers, and the Bey of Tunis, what had the presidents and the commodore accomplished? While the British laughed at American efforts, while the French laughed, while the pirates themselves laughed—well, at least *Constellation* could do something right here and now!

She did. For a half hour, despite counterattack from galleys and shore batteries, the frigate delivered considerable damage. Her guns routed the shore troops . . . star-and-crescent banners galloped from the scene. This brought cheers from the young officers and older gunners raining American cannon balls on the Turks.

One of those balls—and of course Tom always believed it came from his 12-pounder—killed the Bashaw's favorite general as he stood on the beach. But since, as the gunner's check later showed, *Constellation* hurled some sixty round shot, as well as twenty-two rounds of grape and twenty-one of canister, who could say which missile carried the fatal message?

As the battle ended and *Constellation* hauled off, Tom felt much better than at any time since entering the Mediterranean. He appreciated how much the action boosted Captain Murray's feelings too when, next day, *Constellation* sailed close to the city and the Tripolines, to quote the Captain's report to Secretary Smith, "did not honor us with another salute!"

Tom admired Captain Murray's firm stance on all the occasions he had faced the Barbary nations. Caesar Rodney also would have approved, Tom realized. But standing offshore on guard, with only occasional face-to-face encounters, would take forever to sweep piracy out of the Mediterranean. What else was Commodore Morris doing?

As *Constellation* sailed into autumn on what seemed the same never-ending, futile patrol, Tom's spirits flagged. The thought of making lieutenant buried itself deep; on a tedious cruise like this, with so little action, he could never hope to perform with the distinction that would merit promotion.

Up and down the Tripoli coast . . . to Malta for supplies . . . back to Tripoli . . . to Palermo . . . over to Tunis. Back to Palermo and on to Naples. To Leghorn . . . here the monotony changed for a few hours while the frigate searched for *Enterprise*'s gig which, in the aftermath of fresh gales, had upset two miles off her larboard quarter; the midshipman in command and three sailors survived, but three others never again appeared, nor did the gig.

In October, *Constellation* visited Toulon; in November, she put into Malaga; she ended the year 1802 at Gibraltar.

Following an appearance off Morocco and Algiers, she departed the Mediterranean.

"Having accomplished very little!" To Caesar Rodney at Cool Spring, Tom expressed the opinion of a large part of the Navy.

Mr. Rodney nodded in agreement.

"Back here at home, everyone looked for great things from Commodore Morris's squadron," he said. "But for all practical purposes you succeeded only in irritating Tunis and Algiers and Morocco with a blockade that had no real effect on Tripoli. You know," he added, "that we paid Tripoli $35,000 to ransom *Franklin*'s crew?"

Not only did Europe still laugh at American efforts to sweep piracy off the Mediterranean . . . now a large part of the United States Congress also thought the Navy wasted its time patrolling! Through scuttle butt, Tom had learned that Commodore Morris probably would find himself suspended for ineffectual handling of the situation.

"Don't let it get you down," his brother James counseled at home. "Personally, you've done all right. On top of good experience in *Ganges,* you've trained on one of the Navy's best frigates. You know how to sail a ship, how to handle a gun and, as near as I can make out, how to handle yourself. You've tamed down just about the right amount. What happened? Did Captain Murray have you flogged?"

Yes, somewhere along the line, perhaps in learning to obey the orders of a superior without feeling any sense of inferiority, Tom had discovered how to control himself. He didn't rush into things rashly any more; he figured out ahead of time what to do, then did it.

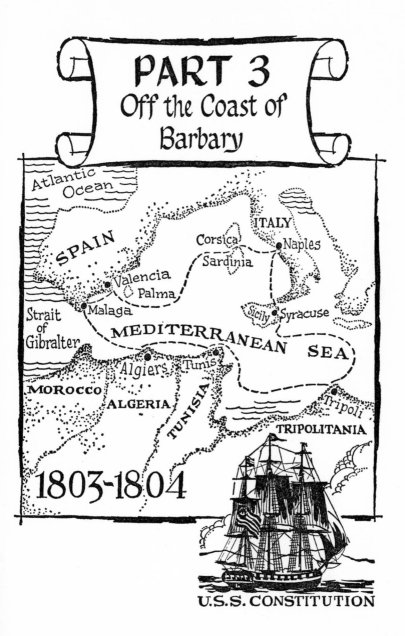

PART 3
Off the Coast of Barbary

Atlantic Ocean

SPAIN

ITALY

Corsica

Sardinia

Naples

Valencia

Palma

Strait of Gibralter

Malaga

MEDITERRANEAN

Sicily

Syracuse

SEA

Algiers

Tunis

MOROCCO

ALGERIA

TUNISIA

Tripoli

TRIPOLITANIA

1803-1804

U.S.S. CONSTITUTION

Having helped lay *Constellation* up at Washington on her return from the Mediterranean, in March of 1803, Midshipman Thomas Macdonough enjoyed a long leave with his family.

"As I wrote," he began one evening after supper, "we—"

"Why, Tom, you sent us only two letters in a year and a half!"

Tom looked at Hester shamefaced.

"I had to do so much other writing . . . ship's log and so forth. Honestly, I thought I wrote you every week or so."

"How can you say such a thing?" Hester kissed him fondly, and forgave.

He patted her hand, and went on, talking continuously, it seemed to him, for the two months of his leave.

Returning to Washington, 22 May, he stopped to visit Caesar Rodney again. Mr. Rodney had good news.

"The President and the Congress have reached their limit with the Barbary states," he confided. "A new squadron will go out to fight them, under Captain Edward Preble."

Tom sat up in his leather-covered library chair. He'd heard much about Preble—tough, a disciplinarian like Truxton and Mullowney and Murray, only more so. The United States apparently had its back up. And with America's back up, the Navy could take on and subdue the Barbary pirates whether

England and France and all the other tribute-paying European powers laughed or not. Tom felt good.

"That's great!"

Then the axe fell.

Reporting on board *Constellation* in high spirits next day, Midshipman Macdonough—veteran of Caribbean and Mediterranean fighting—found a letter from the Navy Department. It ordered him detached from the frigate . . . furloughed until called for. In effect, the Secretary had thrown him out of the Navy—again!

But why now, when Congress had its hackles up and planned to wipe the Barbary pirates off the seas? What kind of craziness went on in the Navy Department? Had Rex Otis and the others felt so angry when they left the ship?

Reeling, Tom packed his gear. Most of his berthmates already having departed, paid off by Purser Keith Spence, goodbys took no time. He flung his visored cap into his bag and clapped the old straw on his head. Saluting the quarterdeck and crossing *Constellation*'s gangplank for the last time, he pretended he was stepping on shore at Havana or Malta.

The moment he set foot on shore, he laughed wryly . . . it felt just as hot here in Washington as it had felt in Havana and Malta! Still seething, he had no objective beyond finding a place to eat, catching the stage north, and making his way home. En route, he'd decide what to tell his family and what to do on a farm after two years at sea working to make lieutenant. You never knew one minute, did you, what the next would bring?

Walking to the stage station, Tom calmed down. The situation called for a little thought. No use to run off home. Why not, in view of Caesar Rodney's confidential information about Captain Preble's fleet, go to the Navy Department and ask Secretary Smith to reconsider his case? Better to take affirmative action than to slink away nursing resentment. Right!

Hat shoved back on his head at an angle that Captains

Murray·and Mullowney would have frowned upon, he left his bag at the stage station and strode in the direction of the Navy Department.

In the Secretary's anteroom, he took off his battered straw and held out the detachment order the Department had sent him.

"I'm Midshipman Thomas Macdonough," he told the Secretary's assistant incisively. "I'd like another ship. I—"

Charles Washington Goldsborough smiled.

"I remember you very well, Mister Macdonough," he said. "And before you hang me on a yardarm read this." Into Tom's hand he thrust a letter which Secretary Smith apparently had just signed.

Tom's eyes skimmed over the still-unsealed letter . . . "recalled from furlough . . . report to frigate *Philadelphia* at Philadelphia . . ."

His heart took a great leap.

". . . Captain William Bainbridge . . . proceed to the Mediterranean . . . part of Commodore Edward Preble's squadron . . ."

His furlough had lasted less than an hour!

With a wave of thanks to Goldsborough, Tom floated happily from the Navy Department office to meet the day's third surprise. Halfway down the steps to the street, he saw his straw hat on another man's head.

"Lieutenant Decatur!"

Striding up the steps, Decatur seemed bent on duty. But at Tom's shout he beamed, and for the first time Tom appreciated what a good-looking man this was . . . wavy dark hair and sideburns framing a long, straight nose and partly hiding large ears. Only four years older than Tom, he looked considerably more. He held out his hand.

"*Como se va?*" he greeted with a Caribbean accent.

Decatur's strong handclasp showed Tom that here stood a country boy like himself. Two inches shorter than Tom, he packed tremendous strength in broad shoulders and powerful legs. He had quite a reputation in the Navy as a swimmer, having dived overboard from frigate *United States* to save a seaman who'd tumbled out of her rigging. He seemed truly glad to see Tom.

"Did Secretary Smith assign you to *Argus?*" he asked.

"To *Philadelphia.* Why?"

"Wait here," Decatur ordered. "I'll be right back."

He went up the remaining steps two at a time, leaving Tom to wonder why, having talked to this man just twice for a total of not more than ten minutes, he liked him so much. Not because of his reputation, because Tom had liked the lieutenant before he knew much about Stephen Decatur, Jr. Only after their first meeting had Tom learned that this was the son of one of the Navy's first captains, Stephen Decatur, Sr., who'd had *Philadelphia* for flagship in the Caribbean the year Tom sailed in *Ganges.*

Something in the way Decatur looked at you, something in the way he held himself as though he knew where he wanted to go and had figured how to get there . . . this combination of qualities Tom liked. Too, apparently, Decatur liked the cut of Tom's jib.

In ten minutes the lieutenant returned, shaking his head.

"I'm taking *Argus* over to the Med," he said as casually as if he planned to go by ferry across Chesapeake Bay. "But the Secretary hasn't signed my orders yet."

He noted Tom's puzzlement.

"Sorry," he said. "Since you're going in *Philadelphia,* I assumed you knew all about plans for the new squadron."

An hour later Tom did know—after Decatur had marched him to Ford's Hotel and sat him down at a table in the dining room where they could eat and talk. Tom learned, in brief, that:

Congress in February had ordered construction of shoal-draft brigs *Argus* and *Siren* and schooners *Nautilus* and *Vixen*

—designed to support American frigates in fighting the Barbary pirates, going after enemy gunboats close inshore.

He, Decatur, would cross the Atlantic in *Argus,* turn her over to Lieutenant Isaac Hull, and take for his command schooner *Enterprise.*

In *Constitution,* Commodore Preble would command the new squadron.

For the most part, Decatur pointed out, the vessels still had their crews to enlist and their stores to get on board. They had spars and guns to ship and mount. As each finished her preparations, she would put to sea to rendezvous in the Mediterranean.

"Now we'll see some action!" declared Tom.

He didn't realize how emphatically he'd expressed himself until he caught the glint in his companion's eyes and saw the broadening smile on his wide mouth. Decatur laughed appreciatively.

"I should have you with me."

"I'd like nothing better." If only Decatur *would* get him on board *Argus!*

Much as he wished he could ask the lieutenant to speak to Secretary Smith, he felt the first move should come from the brig's commander. Obviously, however, Decatur had no intention of making such a move.

"You'll find *Philadelphia* a good ship," he said, and added, "Pay my respects to Captain Bainbridge, if you will. I had the pleasure of serving as his first lieutenant in *Essex* two years ago."

Tom smiled, recalling the international incident that Bainbridge and Decatur had created at Barcelona where Spanish guards fired on an *Essex* boat and Decatur offered to cut off their captain's ears.

When Tom reported to *Philadelphia,* lying in the Delaware River off the barracks, he found the frigate alive with former

Constellation midshipmen and joined Rex Otis, Jim Gibbon, Dan Patterson, Jim Biddle, and Bernie Henry—all recalled from furlough—in the starboard berth. The six made themselves comfortable, as became such experienced officers of the United States Navy.

They'd all come far since they first visited foreign soil and heard sailors, rowing the liberty boat, joke:

"Here come our brave young gentlemen, like the little end of nothing whittled down to a point . . . be careful, boys, or the natives will eat you without salt or pepper." And the same seamen's admonition about the cocked hats which, for the first time, the midshipmen sported: "Slew your air-choppers fore and aft, young gentlemen, or you'll never get on shore against this head wind!"

For their motto these good companions now had that motto of every other midshipmen's berth where the occupants had seen service in the Mediterranean:

"*E Pluribus Unum*—the eagle's flight is out of sight!"

Philadelphia's fitting out proved old stuff to Tom over the long summer weeks, although he saw much new.

Captain Bainbridge showed himself a serious, cultured man, with much charm, in addition to having the physical strength of any other three men on board. He had commanded a ship at nineteen, in the Dutch trade, and had won his fair share of brawls. Though he'd come up the hard way, he kept a velvet glove over his fist of steel.

A first-rate seaman and a rigid master, according to Decatur who seemed to have thrived under him, he'd had the bad luck during the sea-war with France to mistake two French frigates for friendly vessels. They'd forced him to surrender his 14-gun schooner *Retaliation*.

He also smarted from having had to take *George Washington* on that ignominious errand from the Dey of Algiers to the Sultan of Turkey. Though the Sultan had saluted him with honor as the representative of a new nation—while giving the Algerine ambassador scant courtesy—Bainbridge still carried the scars on his spirit.

From what Tom could observe between the time he joined the frigate and she sailed for the Mediterranean, 28 July, Captain Bainbridge looked forward to another go at the pirates with Commodore Preble.

So did *Philadelphia's* officers, midshipmen, crew—and her marines. Largely because of his liking for Dennis Kelly of *Ganges* and the late, lamented duelist James McKnight in *Constellation,* Tom had developed great respect for marines. This despite underlying wariness between sailors and these soldiers of the sea who made up about one-tenth of the ship's company. He'd never quite lost his amazement—and amusement—over the way they wore their high leather stock, on duty and off. How could they stand this neckpiece?

The marines said they wore it because it compelled a recruit to hold his head high; Tom's berthmates insisted the marines wore it to hide the dirt, and called them leathernecks. Anyway, dirty necks or leathernecks, when it came to boarding a pirate ship Tom wanted them along. He had still to see marines fight from the tops, picking off enemy officers with their muskets at close range and tossing grenades down open enemy hatches, but he'd heard plenty about how efficiently they did that, too.

Philadelphia's outfitting proceeded slowly but thoroughly. On 3 July, her hands shipped topmasts and took in spars, lumber, and rigging.

On 12 July, she dropped downriver to Fort Penn where she lay several days, taking in her thirty-six guns.

Off New Castle, she took in water and provisions. Here First Lieutenant Richard B. Jones came on board from New York with the recruits he'd enlisted for two years at wages of ten dollars a month for able-bodied seamen and five dollars to eight dollars for boys and ordinary seamen.

On 28 July, *Nautilus* having sailed earlier, *Philadelphia* dropped her pilot outside Delaware Bay, second of Commodore Preble's squadron off for the Barbary wars.

☆☆☆ CHAPTER 18

From the moment *Philadelphia* put to sea, Tom enjoyed every waking hour. With a wind sail rigged on deck to scoop the Atlantic's cool breezes and funnel them down through a succession of gratings to Midshipmen's Country far below in steerage, he and his fellow veterans of *Constellation* had set up a neat berth.

Bulkheads painted yellow to brighten the space, living quarters contained a table and lockers covered with oilcloth. A buffet held cutlery, glass tumblers, china dishes and teacups, and plated dish covers. Two swing lamps hung from the deck overhead; against one bulkhead swung a china pitcher with water and a washbasin, in gimbals, like a compass. In their "sequestered grove and shady retreat," the midshipmen took their ease.

The frigate made good time to Gibraltar, arriving 24 August, after a passage through the Strait that included the horseplay Tom had undergone when he first passed the Pillars of Hercules. He laughed at how mad other midshipmen became when Neptune's barber shaved their heads. They'd get over it!

Immediately on anchoring, Captain Bainbridge received word of two pirate cruisers on the coast of Spain, half-way between Malaga and Cartegena, off Cape de Gata. Gossip had it, too, that England had become concerned over growing American commerce in the Mediterranean, so that she now paid extra tribute to Tripoli to encourage piracy. *Philadelphia* put out after the corsairs.

She made good time along the rugged coast which, now and then, rose to a range of mountains like the Sierra Nevadas whose snow caps at almost 12,000 feet glistened white in the brilliant sun. Enjoying the view, Tom heard a lookout call that he saw a vessel flying Barbary colors. Falling off in chase, *Philadelphia* hoisted British colors—a common trick of the times.

Overhauling, she fired several guns before her quarry came to. Within hailing distance at sunset, Captain Bainbridge ordered a seaman who could speak the *lingua franca* of the Mediterranean—Italian mixed with French, Spanish, Greek, and Arabic—to ask her name.

"Meshboah," came the reply from her captain, a shabby, wild-eyed Moor.

"Where from?"

"Morocco."

"Where bound?"

"Morocco."

"What news?"

"The Emperor has given us orders to capture all American vessels."

"Have you taken any?"

"Yes, we've captured a brig."

"What name?"

"Celia, of Boston."

"Where is she?"

"Ahead."

"Are any of her men on board you?"

"Yes, the captain and four seamen."

At this, *Philadelphia* dropped the British ensign and hoisted

American colors. The consternation that fell on the grisly pirate crew gave Tom great satisfaction for days afterward.

Lieutenant John Cox went in a boat to look the prize over. Returning with a grim expression on his usually cheerful countenance, he brought with him the vessel's seedy-looking captain.

On the quarter-deck, Captain Bainbridge bristled.

"Morocco has a peace treaty with the United States!"

The Moorish captain shrugged and pulled a paper from the folds of his robe. Deciphered, the document gave him authority to seize American ships. Signed by the governor of Tangier, it flagrantly violated the treaty.

Captain Bainbridge released the members of *Celia*'s crew whom Lieutenant Cox had found in chains on board *Meshboah*. And while he dealt with the Moorish captain, word got around among *Philadelphia*'s midshipmen that *Celia* had on board a chorus of slave girls en route to the Sultan of Turkey, to dance in his light opera company and entertain his harem. Midshipman Macdonough didn't get to see the Sultan's dancing girls, but he did see dancing.

Ordered on board *Meshboah* with Lieutenant Cox and a prize crew, he found the miserable Moroccan ship literally jumping with vermin. He later described the vessel, for whose capture Congress appropriated $5,000 in lieu of prize money, as "a miserable piece of naval architecture with thirty badly mounted guns—a filthy hulk loaded with onions. I wouldn't have taken her across the Atlantic for fifty thousand dollars!"

With *Celia* in convoy, *Meshboah* next day turned toward Gibraltar, and from her deck Tom watched *Philadelphia* haul off for Tripoli. When, he wondered, would he see the frigate again?

Weather played tricks en route to Gibraltar.

For a few hours fog would drop down, so thick that the ship and the brig could keep in touch only by blowing on their horns. A few hours later, the fog would lift; the sun then would beat down so hot that Tom sought any shelter that sails or spars afforded. To go belowdecks proved more than he could stomach, what with Moorish stench and animal life that infested the hold. He slept on deck.

Off Malaga, he caught sight of the Rock of Gibraltar, like a blue cloud. Rounding Europa Point and the British fortress, under which moored a British squadron, the captive ship and the Boston brig sailed across the bay to the Algiciras roads for safe anchorage against winds out of the west while awaiting the arrival of Commodore Preble and instructions for the vessels' disposition.

From *Meshboah*'s rail, Tom got a leisurely view of Algiciras, a town of white houses with a single, steepled church. North of the town, Fort Santiago lay close to the water, and the cemetery, near the summit of a cliff, had a small chapel within its white walls. Tom did not go on shore, for two good reasons.

First, from long experience with seamen, Lieutenant Cox refused to invite trouble by letting his prize crew land; second, they could buy anything they needed from the bumboats that swarmed alongside.

Mostly rowed out from shore—a few sailed with patched canvas—the bumboats offered a variety of fruits, vegetables, carved wood religious statues, furs, cheap perfume, and gimcracks. Having picked up enough trading Spanish in the Caribbean to act as interpreter for his companions, Tom enjoyed bargaining for every piece of jewelry and for every vegetable. Trading served to pass the time, since Lieutenant Cox had properly decided that to try to clean up *Meshboah* would only contaminate his men. Better let sleeping bugs lie!

At last, into Gibraltar Bay, 12 September, sailed U.S. frigate *Constitution,* looking even more impressive than when Tom first saw her from *Ganges'* deck in mid-Atlantic. She had cost $300,000 to build, and she gave off an aura of quality. Two hundred and four feet overall, mounting long 24-pounders and 12-pounders and 32-pounder carronades, she looked every inch a flagship. Something of Commodore Preble's own disciplined pride and strength emanated from her sides— twenty-two inches thick at the waterline, sturdy enough to bounce iron balls off. Her figurehead, carved by Simon Skillings of Boston, was, properly, of Hercules.

In Tom's ears, the salute that *Constitution* fired as she entered the bay told Europe's nations in booming tones that they would laugh no longer at America's efforts to wipe piracy off the seas. Not with ships like *Constitution;* not with a commodore like Edward Preble!

☆☆☆ CHAPTER 19

Rowed across Gibraltar Bay with Lieutenant Cox to report to Commodore Preble, Tom took deep breaths in an effort to keep his heart from racing as it always did in times of stress. For Commodore Preble, frosty-eyed and ramrod stiff, had all sorts of names put on him by all sorts of people. Those who knew him best—who had served under him—called him intrepid, courageous, daring, brilliant. All these epithets he merited.

At twenty, serving in the Revolution as first lieutenant on the Boston sloop-of-war *Winthrop,* he'd led fourteen men to capture a British brig in the Penobscot River, in Maine where he grew up. He'd had fifteen years as merchant skipper before going into the war with France as first lieutenant in *Constitu-*

tion. Wanting more action, he'd secured command of brig *Pickering,* then of frigate *Essex.* Against the Barbary pirates, he'd patrolled the Mediterranean in corvette *Adams* until ill health had taken him from the Navy.

Now he returned to provide the driving power the new squadron needed to accomplish what Commodores Dale and Morris had failed to achieve.

Hard as a teak log and just as communicative, so his relatives said, Edward Preble came by his special qualities honestly. As a boy he'd seen a ship in Falmouth with a Turk on board, and his father had filled him and his brother with the idea that Turks ate little boys. His father then paid the Turk to appear on the Preble doorstep one night after the parents had left the boys alone. When the Turk, enjoying the prank, began to gibber, Edward's brother ran to hide under the bed. But not Edward. He grabbed a burning stick out of the fireplace and threw it into the Turk's face!

Young officers fitting out their vessels in Philadelphia had called Preble a sourpuss. With a short temper sharpened by uncertain health, and having no truck with the young gentlemen's dueling code of honor, he seemed a rough diamond. Always appearing to look down his nose in quiet New England fashion, he ruffled the fine feathers of officers from Virginia and thereabouts.

He'd shown his displeasure over Navy Department orders for the various ships in his new fleet to sail separately to the Mediterranean instead of going together under his eagle eye, drilling as a squadron. Realizing that each ship would remain a world unto itself with their young commanders—all thirty years or under—showing off their paces, Preble had dubbed them boys . . . young cubs. This had not endeared him to his captains.

But the midshipman who brought the message to *Meshboah* for Lieutenant Cox and Midshipman Macdonough to report on board the flagship uncorked a new feeling about the Commodore, a feeling of unadulterated admiration.

With pride he related how, a few nights earlier, as *Constitution* approached Cape Trafalgar, the lookout had reported a light, visible for only a second or two. Shortly afterward a sail shaped up in the blackness and, at the creak of a gun port, *Constitution*'s four hundred-plus company sprang to life. Taking the deck, Commodore Preble sent his men to quarters, passing the word sharply without bugle, pipe, or drum. He then hailed the stranger through his trumpet:

"What ship is that?"

No answer.

The crew considered whether the shape might be an island or a reef. But it moved at *Constitution*'s own speed, so it had to be a ship. Commodore Preble hailed again.

Again no answer.

Angrier every minute at this strange-acting vessel, the Commodore came to a boil. He roared across the open water:

"I hail you for the last time. If you do not answer I will fire a shot into you."

That brought a response.

"If you fire, I shall return a broadside," came a voice through the night.

"I'd like to see you do it!" Preble bellowed. "I now hail you for an answer. What ship is that?"

"This is His Britannic Majesty's ship *Donegal,* eight-four guns, Sir Richard Strahan, commodore. Send your boat on board!"

Officers close to Commodore Preble thought he'd hit the mizzenmast top at this outrageous order. Leaping into the hammock nettings, he grabbed the mizzen shrouds and thundered, "This is the United States frigate *Constitution,* fifty-five guns, Edward Preble, an American commodore, who'll be damned before he sends his boat on board any vessel. Blow your matches, boys!"

In that instant, Edward Preble won the affection of every officer and seaman on board the flagship. Sourpuss, nothing! This was a man after their own hearts. Ready to take on anybody—fifty-five guns to eighty-four! He drove hard; he got mad; he flew into rages. But what a man to fight under!

Backing down, the British captain had rowed over to the American flagship. He disclosed that his vessel, frigate *Maidstone* of only thirty-two guns, had found herself caught off guard, her officers asleep. He apologized.

Commodore Preble received Lieutenant Cox and Midshipman Macdonough in the very spacious quarters of *Constitution*'s after gun deck. He did the pair the honor of shaking hands when they entered. With his flag lieutenant, he put them at ease. Then he seated himself at a big mahogany table. Hatched-faced, to Tom he looked neither old nor young as he listened to Lieutenant Cox's report on *Philadelphia*'s encounter with the Moroccan corsair and its captive American brig.

Before making any comment, the Commodore rubbed his long nose and glared out a stern gallery window. When he responded, Tom got a sharply defined picture of the Mediterranean scene as Edward Preble saw it.

"The President designed this fleet of ours to impress the Barbary pirates. He wants us to keep this sea clear so that our merchantmen can trade freely with any nation they wish to do business with. My squadron, my officers, my men" . . . he emphasized the *my* in each case with a shade of affection surprising in so tough a commander . . . "will do just that. We'll let these corsairs know in short order just how much weight we can throw against them. From the news you gentlemen bring, I think we'd better start with the Moroccans."

He added, "We'll clean up this sea one pirate nation at a time."

That ended the interview.

A few days later, on signal from *Constitution,* Midshipman Macdonough reported again to flag quarters. This time Commodore Preble let him stand at attention in front of the table. Finally:

"Mister Macdonough, I have decided to return *Meshboah* to the Emperor of Morocco," the Commodore announced. As Tom's face dropped, he quickly added, "In person!"

Tom understood. Commodore Preble intended to make the Emperor live up to his treaty with the United States, thus impressing the first of the four pirate nations with America's determination to stop piracy—and her power to do it.

Of a sudden Tom felt a chill. Did Commodore Preble plan, after delivering *Meshboah,* to leave him in the Emperor's service?

Constitution led an impressive squadron through the Strait of Gibraltar into the Atlantic Ocean as she escorted *Meshboah* to the Emperor of Morocco.

Off the capital city of Tangier, with an American flotilla that included frigate *New York,* corvette *John Adams,* and new shoal-draft *Nautilus* fresh from the United States, Commodore Edward Preble went to work. And Midshipman Macdonough followed each move of the American naval commander with mounting admiration for the subtle effectiveness of his country's inherent strength when directed by a man of decision.

Having received word of the Americans' coming, the Emperor of Morocco rode into his capital with an army of ten thousand men on 6 October.

With cold courtesy, the Commodore dressed his powerful array of warships for the occasion . . . *Constitution* fired a twenty-one gun salute.

The Emperor's fort fired an answering salute.

On the second day, the Emperor sent the frigate a gift of ten bullocks, sheep, and fowl.

On the third day, the Emperor marched his army down to the waterfront for a long, hard look at the visitors.

On the fourth day, the Emperor opened negotiations— convinced that Commodore Preble could back words with deeds.

Receiving the Emperor's assurances that Morocco's friend- ship with the United States would last forever, Commodore Preble returned *Meshboah* with impressive lack of comment.

In Tom's estimation, Commodore Preble's quiet accomplish- ment spoke loudly to a scoffing world. In three weeks he'd found evidences of piracy, taken the captured proof to the offending nation, achieved peace.

And, departing, he left *Nautilus* to keep a realistic eye on the Moroccan coast.

☆☆☆ CHAPTER 20

Tom left Tangier in *Constitution*.

Passenger on board the flagship and often invited to dine in her wardroom, he absorbed a good deal from the frigate's officers. The Commodore, too, treated him somewhat as a guest while deciding where to assign him to duty. Serious-faced and open-eared, Tom felt as though he were attending school, taught by the headmaster himself. His course: American for- eign policy, with special attention to the strategy of eliminating piracy from the Mediterranean.

In keeping the Mediterranean free for merchant ships of

the United States, the Commodore wrote to all his captains: "You are to respect the rights of nations with whom we are at peace, and not to capture vessels within the jurisdictional limits or under the protection of such nations."

He told them, also: "You are at all times, as far as may be in your power, to succour and relieve and free any American vessel attacked by the enemy or in their possession."

So much for general policy.

Pacing his quarters, the Commodore in person gave Tom a nut-shell summary of how he proposed to put teeth into that policy.

"Our strategy comes down to a blockade of the strongest pirate nation—Tripoli."

Using all the ships at his command, he intended to stop Tripoli's piracy and Tripoli's trade at the same time—allowing no vessel to pass either in or out of the country.

"Successful blockade of Tripoli will force all the corsairs to appreciate two facts of life," he declared. "First, that America can marshal enough naval might to put them out of business whenever necessary. Second . . ." he stopped pacing long enough to hold Tom with his frosty glance . . . "that free trade will pour more gold into their national treasuries than all the prize money they can possibly obtain through piracy."

Tom had a thought, too. If the blockade failed? Well, in addition to making America an even greater laughingstock in Europe, failure would raise hob in Washington which seethed with opinions on how best to cope with the pirates. Tom didn't bring that thought up, however. The Commodore did.

"What if our blockade doesn't work?" He laughed, the first time Tom ever had heard him laugh. "We'll *make* it work."

Calling in his clerk, Commodore Preble dictated a letter for Stephen Decatur who, commanding schooner *Enterprise,* now escorted a merchant convoy to Syracuse in Sicily. After a few preliminaries, Commodore Preble got to the point of the message:

... every vessel will proceed to the Blockade of Tripoli, cruise off that place until the season makes it dangerous ... you must, even in the very worst season, go out and show yourself off Tripoli occasionally, if only for a day or two at a time, as it will have a good effect, by convincing those Barbarians that their vessels are not safe in leaving Port at any season of the year.

Commodore Preble further instructed:

You are to capture all vessels belonging to the Bashaw of Tripoli, or his subjects, and to annoy the enemy by all the means in your power ... You are not to suffer the vessels of any nation to enter or have commerce with Tripoli, but have a right to treat as an enemy whoever may endeavor to enter that place or carry anything to it whilst blockaded by us.

The Commodore now took *Constitution* through the Mediterranean to set up the blockade of Tripoli and to select a nearby neutral port in which the squadron could rendezvous and provision while maintaining the blockade. During the run, much happened.

For one, Tom got a deeper understanding of what made Edward Preble a great leader. It came out of a book in the Commodore's library, by an Athenian historian named Thucydides who had lived and died on the Mediterranean's shores. Tom read:

Our habits of discipline make us both brave and wise; brave, because the spirit of loyalty quickens the sense of honor, and the sense of honor inspires courage; wise, because we are not so highly educated that we have learned to despise the laws. We have not acquired that useless over-intelligence which makes a man an excellent critic of an enemy's plans but paralyzes him in the moment of action.

Let our preparations be not words but deeds. Our hopes ought not to rest on the probability of the enemy making mistakes, but on our own caution and foresight. We should remember that one man is much the same as another, and that he is best who is trained in the severest school.

The Commodore had underlined *"he is best who is trained in the severest school."* Tom recognized that he'd had his basic lessons under good teachers.

The second happening came, literally, out of a clear sky. As *Constitution* proceeded toward Tripoli, she spoke English frigate *Amazon* off the southwest end of Sardinia. The Britisher gave a few bare facts:

A month earlier, 31 October, American frigate *Philadelphia* had gone on a reef in Tripoli harbor . . . pirates had captured her and thrown officers and men into prison!

Tom felt as though a mountain had fallen on him. What about Rex Otis? And—Tom realized that Commodore Preble, having entire responsibility for the squadron, must feel the blow even more.

Off the harbor of Malta, 27 November, Commodore Preble received letters from Captain Bainbridge giving particulars of *Philadelphia*'s catastrophe. She had gone into the harbor after a pirate xebec, sounding as she went. The water shoaled . . . turning seaward, she struck a hidden reef. She had jettisoned anchors and guns, but failed to float off. In the face of certain death for all, she had struck her colors!

While Commodore Preble mulled over *Philadelphia*'s loss, *Constitution* labored in a heavy northwest gale that whipped up tremendous seas. Under reefed courses and storm staysails she fetched up under the lee of Sicily, in smooth water. Here she fell in with *Enterprise* which reported that store ship *Traveller* had reached the nearby port of Syracuse. Tom acted at once—before the frigate and the schooner entered Syracuse for provisioning next morning.

He respectfully asked the Commodore for assignment to *Enterprise*.

Commodore Preble looked him over quizzically.

"What do you know about Lieutenant Decatur?"

"I met him, sir, in the Caribbean."

"He runs a very taut ship."

"I understand he runs a school as severe as your own, sir."

Of a sudden, Commodore Preble's face warmed. He looked at Tom like a proud father.

"Pack your gear, boy," he said quietly. "I'll sign your orders at once."

Tom went on board *Enterprise* in the harbor of Syracuse, 14 December. He transferred from *Constitution* in a barge rowed by eight seamen and steered by Midshipman Morris who declared that no one in his right mind would leave the flagship for a 12-gun schooner.

"And why that straw hat on a chilly day like this?"

The dilapidated hat did exactly what Tom hoped. It brought Lieutenant Decatur to the quarter-deck rail.

Tom handed over his orders from Commodore Preble.

"Come to my cabin," said Decatur.

If Tom had liked the man on their two previous meetings, he liked him even better on this. And though *Enterprise*'s commander told him to sit at ease, he had the good judgment to hold his tongue and listen.

"First of all, Mister Macdonough," said Decatur with official seriousness, "I shall expect you to know and to carry out your proper duty on this vessel under Lieutenants James Lawrence, Joseph Bainbridge—Captain Bainbridge's younger brother—and Jonathan Thorn. Your fellow midshipmen include George Mitchell and Walter Boyd. Lewis Heerman's our surgeon's mate. Our crew numbers eighty-nine at the moment."

Decatur looked into the distance, seemed on the verge of saying more, thought better of it, and rose to end the brief interview.

At *Enterprise*'s rail that afternoon, watching her take in the fresh meat, vegetables, fruit, rice, and candles which Syracuse offered in abundance, Tom looked up to find Lieutenant Decatur beside him.

Decatur's dark eyes held their usual friendly gleam.

"Will you give me the pleasure of your company at dinner on shore tonight, Mister Macdonough?"

"I will consider it an honor, sir," said Tom, and saluted.

That evening Tom paid less attention to food than in trying to learn what Decatur had on his mind. Nearing dessert—a Sicilian delicacy lost on Tom—the Lieutenant threw out a question.

"How well do you remember *Philadelphia?*"

Tom sat up. He remembered every locker on board the captured frigate.

"What can we do about her?"

The question caught Tom by surprise although, like everyone else in *Constitution* and *Enterprise,* he'd racked his brain for the past week to answer it. He opened his mouth to try again.

But the moustachioed waiter, coming to the table with coffee, broke the conversational thread and Decatur let the subject drop. Tom sat the rest of the evening out silently, respecting the lieutenant's unusual preoccupation and giving free rein to his own reflections on how to get Rex Otis and *Philadelphia*'s company out of pirate hands.

With Decatur still preoccupied, Tom walked with the lieutenant slowly along the waterfront toward the captain's gig that waited to ferry them back to *Enterprise*. In the dark of the quiet night, he continued to seek a solution to *Philadelphia*'s plight. If they could—

Two men leaped from a shadow—behind, Tom sensed a third—then Decatur's voice as he drew his sword and slashed.

"Bandits, Tom! At 'em!"

Midshipman Macdonough never had used his sword, a present from Caesar Rodney, but naval practice called for officers to wear one on shore. Wishing he had a pistol instead, Tom flailed, turning in a three-hundred-and-sixty degree circle to cover front and back. The action filled him with tremendous excitement. Swinging his blade, he felt like Samson with the ass's jawbone.

The Sicilian attackers must have anticipated resistance, but not so fast and not so much. Knife still raised, one fell with Decatur's sword through his stomach. Decatur shouted. Tom turned on the man behind—just in time. As though to cut the bandit off at the waist, he slashed. The man fled. Blood boiling, Tom chased—up the street and over a wall. Running, he became deadly calm.

When his quarry hauled himself up onto a shed and from that to the roof of an adjoining house, Tom closed in. And then, at the far edge of the steeply-sloped room, the bandit stumbled and pitched off. His wild cry filled the night . . . Tom heard a sickening thump on cobbles below.

Slowly making his way down the roof, to the shed, to the alley along which he'd come, Tom found Decatur beside the body of the would-be assassin.

"My man fell to his death off a roof," Tom reported.

"I lost the third man," said Decatur, sounding very disappointed.

On board *Enterprise,* the lieutenant motioned Tom toward the captain's quarters.

"You still look pale."

"I'm still scared!"

Decatur's laugh resounded through the ship, almost as loud as the foremast bell.

In his cabin, boots off and glass in hand, he opened up.

"Since you're turning out to be my favorite midshipman," he said, "I'm going to talk frankly about *Philadelphia*. Keep it between us, Tom."

For considerable time, they discussed the frigate's surrender and how her men now lived on stale black bread and olive oil under the lash of overseers who forced them to work on Tripoli's fortifications as slaves. This, Tom knew, Commodore Preble had learned from Nicholas C. Nissen, Danish consul at Tripoli.

Decatur then revealed that letters to Commodore Preble from Captain Bainbridge contained writing in secret ink, and Tom perked up.

"Consul Nissen sends his cook to Bainbridge every day with a basket of delicacies," Decatur revealed. "Occasionally he sends limes or lemons, and Bainbridge uses their juice for invisible ink. After writing a harmless note in ordinary ink on one page of a double sheet, he follows with a secret message on the second page. Nissen's cook carries the sealed letter out of the prison, and heat makes the hidden message legible."

These letters came and would continue to come, Decatur told Tom, via a circuitous route that included overland travel by well-bribed courier to the American consul at Tunis and from there by ship to Preble. Tom recalled seeing one, on the end of a boarding pike, passed from a small boat to *Constitution*'s landing stage.

"I think we should retake *Philadelphia*," Tom said abruptly.

Now Decatur perked up.

"You know that the Tripolines have salvaged her guns, got her off the reef, and repaired her for their own use?"

"I know."

"You think we could bring her out of the harbor?"

"We could try."

Decatur lifted his glass.

"We may have that try!" he confided. *"Enterprise* has orders to accompany *Constitution* to Tripoli."

☆☆☆ CHAPTER 21

Tom remembered Tripoli from his previous patrol in *Constellation*. But he read again what the *Naval Gazeteer* had to say about it:

> TRIPOLI: on the N. coast of Africa, is a populous though not a large place on the S. shore of the Mediterranean, about 90 leagues to the S.E. from Tunis and 90 leagues at E.S.E. from Algiers. The inhabitants are noted pirates; but they have also some trade in stuffs, saffron, corn, oil, wood, dates, ostrich feathers, and skins, though it is agreed they make more of the Christian slaves which they take at sea, either by way of ransom or by making them perform all sorts of work. It is in lat. 32 deg. 54 min. N and long. 13 deg. 5 min. E.

That about said everything, very concisely.

Now Commodore Preble proposed to change the situation. He planned to prevent those stuffs, saffron, corn, oil, ostrich feathers, etc. from going out of Tripoli. He proposed also to prevent foreign supplies from going in.

Constitution and *Enterprise* would be joined by *Vixen* when she returned from carrying dispatches to Gibraltar and by *Siren* when she finished delivering money and presents to the Dey of Algiers.

Because *Nautilus* now cruised off Cape Bon and Tunisian waters while *Argus* kept an eye on the Emperor of Morocco, Commodore Preble would blockade with only four ships—a good trick if he could do it. Particularly since the Bashaw had augmented his large fleet of cruisers and gunboats with frigate *Philadelphia*.

On arriving off Tripoli, Commodore Preble sent a flag on shore, ostensibly to learn how *Philadelphia*'s prisoners fared. The boat that ferried *Constitution*'s lieutenant did several other chores at the same time.

It learned that the Bashaw wanted peace only on outrageous terms; it arranged through the Danish consul for a necessary supply of money for the comfort and health of the prisoners; it determined how many vessels the Bashaw commanded, and where they lay; and it pin-pointed the American frigate's position.

Lieutenant Decatur visited the flagship, 17 December, for a long talk with Commodore Preble. After dinner, following his return, he called *Enterprise*'s officers into his cabin, passed out seegars, and dropped a bombshell into their laps.

"The shore visit," he said flatly, "has convinced Commodore Preble that we cannot hope to bring *Philadelphia* out of the harbor."

Tom felt as though the world had fallen apart. He'd set his heart on recapturing the frigate. Decatur, too, had seemed elated at the prospect. Now—

"But the Commodore has given me the honor," the lieutenant went on evenly, "to head a volunteer party that will go on board the frigate and burn her!"

Tom shouted. Decatur held up a restraining hand.

"Before all you daring young men volunteer for the job, let me point out a couple of things."

For all his joking tone, he looked stern.

"Just remember, for one, that when you have a good dinner

inside you, as now, you can feel very brave. But when you face danger that you deliberately go out and look for, you mostly need experience, not recklessness."

He smiled, as if at a private joke.

"Of course you have to have a natural affinity for excitement. Because if you worry about getting killed, you'll probably end up dead. If you don't think too much about it, the odds are you'll come through."

He paused, observed the group's reactions, and went on:

"Excitement will carry you only so far. The rest of the way you have to go on plain, ordinary guts. Before you volunteer, ask yourself one question: 'Have I the necessary staying power?' "

He looked around the group again.

"Have I any volunteers?" he asked.

A unanimous shout filled the cabin.

Time flew. Tom viewed Tripoli with fresh eyes. Now he saw a city facing north and east on a slight hill, surrounded by intrenchments and enclosed by a wall twenty to thirty feet high —thick, solid, impregnable—above what was a roadstead rather than a landlocked harbor.

At the city's easternmost corner the slender pinnacles of the Bashaw's palace rose on foundations laid twelve hundred years before. On the city's Mediterranean side a thin finger of land, slightly above sea level, descended gradually in a north-easterly line to meet islets that bounded the roadstead on the north.

Vessels did not usually approach Tripoli from the east where lay the reefs on which *Philadelphia* struck. Instead, they entered from the north, through the islets' western passage, close to the finger of land and immediately under the guns of powerful Fort Mandrach on the mole. Altogether, Tripoli mounted one hundred and fifteen pieces of heavy cannon in the hands of twenty-five thousand Arabs and Turks.

The city also had the reported protection of a brig that mounted ten guns; two schooners of eight guns each; nineteen gunboats, each mounting a heavy 18- or 24-pounder in its bow, with two brass howitzers on its quarters, and carrying from thirty-six to fifty men; and two galleys carrying about one hundred men each. Ranged in order of battle, these vessels formed a strong line of defense at secure moorings inside the rocks and shoals that extended more than two miles eastward.

As Tom could well see, the Tripolines lay snug—safe from northern gales and from attack by warships of *Constitution*'s draft. Unless they wished to expose themselves, coming out by way of the many channels and openings of the reefs, they could remain the entire winter like this.

As Tom also could see through Decatur's glass—below the Bashaw's castle, surrounded by reefs, rocks, forts, and warships—*Philadelphia* rode at a protected mooring to which only a native pilot could have guided her, her guns turned against her friends.

On 23 December, *Enterprise* chased a sail flying Turkish colors, overhauled, and recognized her for Tripoline ketch *Mastico,* which had taken part in the attack on *Philadelphia.*

Mastico boasted two cannons on deck and two extra in the hold, once having served as a French gunboat. With a Turk for master, she had seven Greeks and four Turks in crew; her passengers included one Turkish officer, two Tripoline officers, ten Tripoline soldiers, and forty-two Negro men, women, and children going as slaves to a Turkish pasha. Shades of Zero Coffin!

Tom had little time to think back on his long-time enemy from home, however, for *Enterprise* carried the captured ketch into Syracuse as a prize. And on Christmas day Lieutenant Decatur announced that in *Mastico* they'd found the long-sought solution to their problem of destroying *Philadelphia.*

"We'll sail her into Tripoli harbor at night and burn the frigate right under the Turks' noses!"

Sixty feet long with a beam of twelve feet, *Mastico* would arouse no suspicion when she approached the Barbary coast. She looked like a pirate ship and, heaven help Tom during the time he'd have to spend in her, smelled like one. No amount of scrubbing could banish that Moorish stink!

"We'll have to move fast," Decatur told his volunteers.

Already, it appeared, the Tripolines had begun to take Commodore Preble's squadron more seriously than they had taken Dale's or Morris's. Through an agent, the Bashaw had suggested exchanging *Philadelphia* for a schooner, trading sixty of her crew for sixty captured Turks, the balance of the Americans to go free for five hundred dollars ransom each. And no future tribute.

"The Commodore will have no part of that. If the Bashaw already wants peace, he's bound to settle on more reasonable terms later." Decatur paused, impressively. "If, meanwhile, we blow *Philadelphia* up in his face, he'll no doubt capitulate. So let's shake a leg!"

Tom felt good the next busy weeks. Worked so hard he could only turn in at night exhausted, he noted a considerable change in his commanding officer.

Always Decatur had governed his ship's company through their affections rather than their fears. He watched over his men's comfort, sympathized with the hardships of a seaman's life at sea, and had a just regard for their rights and privileges. His men practically worshipped him, wanted to please him.

For their part, his officers held him in highest esteem despite his only just having passed his twenty-fifth birthday. They liked the way he gave them his confidence, explaining what they needed to know and do, and why. Though they never admitted it to anyone but their own group, they also liked the way he exacted more from his officers than from his men.

"Officers have higher aims," he'd told them, "more stringent obligations, and a future which it is within their power to make more brilliant."

Mostly, they liked the pattern of success he had set for himself. With him, they believed, they too would make their future brilliant.

To all this, Tom noted during the weeks in which he helped overhaul *Mastico* for the expedition, Decatur had added a touch of iron. This stemmed directly from Commodore Preble's note after *Enterprise* had sent men on shore for the purpose of fitting *Mastico*'s rigging.

"One of your men," wrote Commodore Preble from *Constitution,* "is in irons on board this ship—for impertinence to me."

To keep rumors from reaching enemy ears, no word about the forthcoming expedition had passed to the crew. The men worked, they thought, at an ordinary job of refitting.

But after Decatur had told his officers that he and Commodore Preble had renamed the ketch *Intrepid,* seamen who heard the new name quickly got a feeling that something big lay in the wind. Why else a name like that for this Mediterranean-rigged tub whose low masts carried lateen sails on yards so long that part of each stuck forward of its mast like a jib?

"Something don't smell right about this," Sailing Master Seth Carter observed to Tom one day as he watched the carpenter and his mates at work.

Not knowing exactly what to say to that, Tom said nothing. Instead, he winked broadly.

☆☆☆ CHAPTER 22

On 31 January 1804, a day to live forever in the memory of Midshipman Thomas Macdonough, Decatur summoned him to the captain's cabin along with *Enterprise*'s officers. Tom sat close to Lieutenants Lawrence and Thorn. First Lieutenant Bainbridge sat at Decatur's right with the ship's surgeon, Lewis Heerman, beside him. All looked stern.

On the desk before Decatur lay a letter which he picked up after a few seconds of momentous silence. Tom remembered long afterward how you could feel that silence the same way you felt a Mediterranean fog . . . it enfolded you.

"This has just come to me from the flagship," said Decatur. "I want you to hear exactly what Commodore Preble has to say to every one of us here." His eyes swept the cabin. To Tom, they'd never looked quite so black, so clear, so piercing. Nor, to Tom, had his commanding officer ever looked quite so much a commander. Decatur's voice filled the cabin:

You are hereby ordered to take command of the prize ketch which I have named the *Intrepid,* and prepare her with all possible despatch for a cruise of 35 days, with full allowance of water and provisions for 75 men. I shall send you five midshipmen from the *Constitution,* and you will take seventy men, including officers from the *Enterprise,* if that number can be found ready to volunteer their services . . .

The officers laughed at the idea that finding volunteers might prove difficult.

. . . for boarding and burning the *Philadelphia,* in the harbor of Tripoli; if not, report to me, and I will furnish you with men to complete your complement. It is expected you will be ready to sail tomorrow evening, or some hours sooner, if the signal is made for that purpose.

It is my order that you proceed to Tripoli, in company with the *Siren,* Lieutenant Stewart, enter the harbor at night, board the *Philadelphia,* burn her, and make good your retreat with the *Intrepid,* if possible, unless you can make her the means of destroying the enemy's vessels in the harbor, by converting her into a fire ship for that purpose, and retreating in your boats, and those of the *Siren.*

You must take fixed ammunition and apparatus for the frigate's eighteen pounders, and if you can, without risking too much, you may endeavor to make them the instruments of destruction to the shipping and the Bashaw's Castle. You will provide all the necessary combustibles for burning and destroying ships.

The destruction of the *Philadelphia* is an object of great importance, and I rely with confidence on your intrepidity and enterprise to effect it. Lieutenant Stewart will support you with the boats of the *Siren,* and cover your retreat with that vessel.

Be sure and set fire in the gun-room berths, cockpit, storeroom forward, and berths on the berth deck. After the ship is well on fire, point two of the 18-pounders, shotted, down the main hatch, and blow her bottom out.

I enclose a memorandum of the articles, arms, ammunition and fireworks necessary, and which you are to take with you. Return to this place as soon as possible and report to me your proceedings.

On boarding the frigate, it is possible you may meet with resistance. It will be well, in order to prevent alarm, to carry all by the sword. May God prosper you in this enterprise.

I have the honor to be, Sir, your obedient servant,
Edward Preble

For seconds no one spoke.

"Well," said Decatur, breaking the silence, "we have about twenty-four hours to make ready for sea."

During the weeks of overhauling, Decatur had had the two guns in *Mastico*'s hold mounted on *Intrepid*'s deck so that she boasted a battery of four ready for service. Provisions too had gone on board. And, while awaiting orders to sail, the officers had gone over and over the jobs that each would do in setting fire to the frigate once they reached her. *Intrepid* now had only to get her supplies of gunpowder and combustibles in.

On *Enterprise*'s quarter-deck, Boatswain John Newman piped all hands aft, where Lieutenant Decatur told them what they now knew by that mysterious shipboard process that silently passes news from captain's cabin to galley through thickest bulkheads. When he called for volunteers, every man stepped forward.

Surgeon's Mate Heerman having previously examined the men, Decatur picked from his data sixty-two, including Gunner William Hook, Marine Sergeant Solomon Wren, and Quartermaster George Brown.

With Decatur, the lieutenants, the surgeon, and the sixty-two men, Tom packed a single change of linen and went on board *Intrepid* where five midshipmen joined them from the flagship: Charles Morris, Ralph Izard, John Rowe, Alexander Laws, and John Davis. Tom knew them all as a lively gang of youngsters, full of fight and well-disciplined. Why else had Commodore Preble selected them himself?

From *Constitution* also came her pilot, Salvatore Catalano.

He had lived under the King of the Two Sicilies at Palermo and knew the harbor at Tripoli as well as he knew his own bed. A garrulous, always-perspiring, bright-eyed, sallow Maltese, who spoke more languages than Tom knew names for, Catalano seemed just about as eager for the expedition as did any of the rosy-cheeked midshipmen.

Decatur came to stand beside Tom at the ketch's rail the evening of 3 February, after three days of watchful waiting for *Constitution*'s signal that would start them on their fateful journey. Tom had heard fleet officers say that Stephen Decatur carried his patriotism and bravery around like medals . . . that he craved fame. But the rapport Tom had established with him told Tom that action, not fame, beckoned Decatur. Fame *followed* the action; it just happened that way.

"Does *Siren* need to come along with us?" Tom asked, gazing toward Lieutenant Stewart's brig, at anchor, her lookouts with their eyes on the flagship's signal staff.

"It's a long story," Decatur replied. "When Charlie Stewart heard about plans to burn *Philadelphia,* he asked Commodore Preble for the assignment. Having already promised me the honor, the Commodore in effect told Charlie that he could come along for the ride."

At that moment the flagship's signalmen went into action. Orders flew over *Intrepid*'s deck. Minutes later she and *Siren* sailed out of the harbor of Syracuse, bound for Tripoli.

Almost at once Tom recalled what Decatur had said that night in the captain's cabin when he first announced the expedition to his officers—about going into danger with courage composed of experience and good nerves. For the wind made up, and the going grew very rough indeed.

☆☆☆ CHAPTER **23**

With five midshipmen and the Maltese pilot, Tom had quarters
belowdecks, starboard, forward of *Intrepid*'s very small cabin
that held Decatur, three lieutenants, and the surgeon.

Midshipmen's Country comprised a platform laid on the
ketch's water casks with so little headroom that Tom's hair
touched the carlings overhead even when he sat down on the
platform. The marines had corresponding accommodations on
the opposite side. The sailors—heaven help them!—lived and
slept in the hold, on top of more casks.

In practically no time, Midshipmen's Country became
insufferable . . . with only the slightest ventilation . . . with
Pilot Catalano exuding a typical Mediterranean aroma which
only admirers of garlic could long endure. Bugs left behind
by Turks and slaves avidly explored new feeding grounds on
the midshipmen.

As if all this were not enough, provisions—when opened—
proved decayed and offensive. Charlie Morris sounded off,
loud and long.

"Some fool gave us the spoiled George Town beef from
Krouse & Co. that Commodore Preble wrote to the Secretary
of the Navy about! None of *Constitution*'s people would eat it.
The casks were the worst sort of fish barrels, very few of them
full-hooped. So the pickle leaked out."

"How do you know all this?" Tom demanded.

"The Commodore put me in charge of public stores."

"Then *you* got this atrocious stuff on board?"

A roar filled the quarters as midshipmen piled on luckless
Charlie Morris.

Tom managed to endure the week it took to cross to the Barbary coast. But his spirits drooped when a typical Mediterranean winter gale swept out of the north and threatened to wreck ketch and brig on Tripoli's beach. He began truly to wonder how much courage he could muster.

Working to windward with her weird Turkish rig, *Intrepid* managed to claw offshore. Lifting, diving, continually in danger of foundering, driven far to the eastward, she battled the sea for another six days. Tom found out that, at least, he had stamina.

Shut out from light and air belowdecks in cramped quarters whose ports he had helped batten down to keep out the battering waves, he suffered from inaction. With no light and little air, with fitful sleep, and with what scraps of food the midshipmen could salvage from spoiled provisions eaten cold because the ketch rolled too hard to fire up the galley stove, he stayed damp and miserable.

Yes, he told himself during those long days and nights of torture, a man can feel very brave with a good dinner inside him and a warm room to eat it in. But hungry and cold and wet . . . he smiled grimly. He'd answered the question Decatur had posed that night. Yes, he did have the staying power to see this through!

The weather finally cleared. The ketch and the brig headed back toward their goal.

☆☆☆ CHAPTER 24

Tom realized that Decatur anticipated no difficulty in approaching Tripoli unsuspected when, on 15 February, Lieutenant Stewart sent a boat to *Intrepid* with Midshipman Thomas O. Anderson and six seamen to share in the forthcoming attack. Anderson reported that *Siren*'s boats would stand ready to take *Intrepid*'s crew out in case the ketch fell under enemy fire from shore batteries.

With *Siren*'s boat in tow now, *Intrepid* looked what she pretended to be—a Tripoline ketch. Ports and guns covered with tarpaulin, *Siren* resembled any merchant brig.

Next afternoon, however, after pleasant weather and smooth sea had favored the expedition all day, Tom noticed *Intrepid* gradually pulling away from *Siren*. In sight of Tripoli harbor, the ketch dared not arouse suspicion by shortening sail or maneuvering strangely. But to carry out agreed rescue plans she needed to keep *Siren* closer at hand.

Decatur therefore ordered *Intrepid*'s spare sails and buckets dragged astern. Thus slowed, the ketch kept up the appearance of a vessel anxious to reach harbor before night.

During the final approach to Tripoli, with a light breeze from the northwest, the midshipmen and all but half-a-dozen crew members stayed belowdecks. From shore, the men working the ship in jackets and fezzes looked like Maltese seamen.

Decatur too wore common sailor jacket and fez, as did pilot Catalano at the wheel. Their sashes hid dirks.

Evening advanced . . . Tom saw the moon start up a clear sky. *Intrepid*'s drags came in. At 7 P.M., she reached the harbor's western entrance.

Plans called for a ten o'clock attack. Worried about delay in reaching the frigate as a result of the wind lightening, as well as difficulty in getting away from her, the pilot urged making the attack at once.

Tom saw Decatur look back at *Siren,* estimating how long she would take to reach a position where she could support *Intrepid* in her retreat. Satisfied that she could gain that station in time, Decatur turned back to Catalano.

"We'll move in now."

Tom's heart picked up its typical time-of-stress beat.

Ever lighter, the wind barely wafted the ketch into the bay. To keep his people's minds busy, Decatur checked over attack plans for the last time:

They would carry spar and gun decks first . . .

Decatur, with Midshipmen Izard and Rowe and fifteen men, would hold the upper deck . . .

Lieutenant Lawrence, with Midshipmen Macdonough and Laws and ten men, would fire the berth deck and forward storeroom . . .

Lieutenant Bainbridge, with Midshipman Davis and ten men, would fire the wardroom and steerage . . .

Midshipman Morris and eight men would fire the cockpit and after storeroom . . .

In the cutter, Midshipman Anderson would take all boats alongside the frigate to cut off any Turks who tried to swim ashore . . .

Lieutenant Thorn, with the surgeon, the gunner, and thirteen men, would guard the ketch . . .

The boarding party would use pikes and axes, resorting to firearms only as a last resort . . .

To help recognize each other in the dark, they would pass the watchword "Philadelphia."

The time, now: 9 P.M.

Waiting in the dark as the minutes dragged, Tom's hand went to the cutlass at his belt. It took very little imagination to appreciate that every foot *Intrepid* ghosted toward the frigate carried him a foot closer to death. His thoughts ran riot. He saw, in the same crazy, imagined scene, his brother James in *Constellation*'s foretop and Rex Otis in the Bashaw's prison.

The low-toned conversations around him trailed off. His mind carried him back to The Trap, to Hester. Was she sewing, mending clothes for the family at this moment? Will Mr. Rodney hear about tonight's expedition? How would it feel to jump onto a deck full of Turks? Tom's hand fell again on his cutlass.

Whispered orders sent boarding officers and men to concealment wherever they could find it while Captain, pilot, and work crew continued to sail *Intrepid*. With *Siren*'s boat still in tow, she continued to resemble an innocent merchantman trying hard to make a difficult mooring in the night. In a variety of clothes that included garments left behind by *Mastico*'s crew, the Americans looked as nondescript as any true seamen from Malta or the Barbary coast.

Calm water reflected the young moon, providing enough light to distinguish prominent objects as the zephyr-like wind continued to waft the ketch ahead. From her bow, huddled close to Charlie Morris, Tom caught his first glimpse of their goal—U.S. frigate *Philadelphia,* now part of the Bashaw's piratical fleet and guarded as treasure.

He saw her as an outline through the darkness, moored broadside to the city and within half a gunshot of the Bashaw's castle and the principal battery. Within easy range also of other harbor batteries, she had the additional protection of three Turk cruisers and twenty gunboats and galleys, fully-manned, in readiness. On top of that, forty of her own guns stood loaded and waiting.

Intrepid slipped past one battery, and Tom now could see *Philadelphia* and the city's white walls clearly. So far, so good.

But how long could the ketch go unsuspected? Did the Turks keep no guard, no watch, on the frigate?

The time: 9:30 P.M.

More silence, and still more. Until Tom began to think he might board *Philadelphia* with no warning raised. If—

A blast of Tripolese battered his ears. On the frigate's bow a turbaned figure came to the rail, angrily hailing the nearly drifting ketch.

To Decatur, who stood easily beside the quartermaster at the wheel, the pilot Catalano translated:

"He wants to know what vessel we are, where we're from, and what we're doing here."

"Tell him we came from Malta." Decatur kept his voice from reaching the frigate's deck. "Say we lost our anchors in the recent gale. Ask permission to make fast to the frigate during the night."

Catalano bellowed the information and followed quickly with a request to tie onto the frigate.

To Tom's amazement, permission came back almost immediately. He felt easier. And then, as the ketch came almost in contact with the frigate, the fickle wind shifted. Swinging directly away from the frigate, it brought smells of the bazaar off the land . . . it brought the ketch to rest abeam of and about twenty yards away from her mark . . . and it flooded Tom's entire body with hot sweat. So close, yet so far away!

Catalano stepped into the breach with a torrent of words.

Under *Philadelphia*'s guns, while Decatur sent crew to *Siren*'s boat, the pilot answered questions about the brig offshore. He said it looked to him like the new man-of-war *Transfer* which the Bashaw had bought from the British at Malta. The last storm must have delayed her. This he told the seamen on *Philadelphia*'s deck at great length and with gestures.

His acting, as he avoided the rays of *Philadelphia*'s lanterns and spun his yarn, would have brought bravos at the San Carlos theater. Calling heaven's vengeance down on the wind that had deserted the ketch at the last moment, he shouted to *Intrepid*'s seamen to pass a line to the boat's crew and implored *Philadelphia* to send a boat out with another line.

Which, to Tom's utter delight, the Turks did.

Watching while the disguised Americans in *Siren*'s boat coupled the two lines, Tom breathed deeply only when both boats returned to their ships and *Intrepid*'s deck crew began to rouse on the line from the frigate. The ketch closed. Decatur had come to her bow now, with Tom and Charlie Morris. Tom once more held his breath as the vessels almost touched . . . another thirty seconds . . . another—

"Americanos!"

☆☆☆ CHAPTER 25

The warning cry shattered Tripoli's quiet. Decatur leaped onto *Philadelphia*'s main chain plates.

"Board!" he commanded as the cry echoed, and gained the frigate's rail.

Ahead of him leaped Charlie Morris; immediately behind, Tom Macdonough. And as a myriad shrieks reverberated in Tom's ears, pandemonium raged on *Philadelphia*'s spar deck.

Shadows lunged with spears, slashed with daggers. In turbans and fezzes, men leaped over the rail nearest shore. Tom saw Decatur's dirk rise at a figure with raised cutlass. He heard the shout "Philadelphia!" Decatur recognized Charlie Morris . . . the dirk stopped in midair.

Because the surprised enemy had no chance to prepare a

defense, the boarders cleared the frigate's spar deck in short order, and Tom saw Decatur stand commander on the quarterdeck his father once had paced. He wondered whether Captain Bainbridge and Rex Otis, and the other wretched prisoners of the Bashaw, yet realized what went on?

When the boarding party also had cleared the gun deck, with Decatur returning to hold the spar deck, Lieutenant Thorn and Gunner Hook passed the combustibles from ketch to frigate.

Tom took up his fire-setting equipment and led Lieutenant Lawrence, Midshipman Laws, and the ten seamen of his party to the berth deck. Already, he noted, belowdecks stank as though the frigate had lain in Turkish hands for centuries.

By the light of improvised torches, his fire party broached kegs of gunpowder, spread oil-soaked rags and waste, and laid combustibles so that they could not fail to burst into flames hot enough to set off *Philadelphia*'s timbers.

As he worked, fast, but with great care—Tom heard the comforting sounds of other parties busy in wardroom, cockpit, steerage, and after storeroom.

Each man had so learned his duties that it seemed mere seconds, once his group reached the forward storeroom, before Tom made ready to put flame to fuses. Waiting for Decatur's command, via Lieutenant Lawrence who listened intently for it, Tom sensed from distant shouting that one of the other parties had run into trouble.

He waited . . . an eternity. Through hatches and gratings, Decatur's order finally filtered down to the berth deck . . . Lieutenant Lawrence gave Tom the signal . . . Tom moved fast.

"To you, Rex!"

Touching torch to well-laid train of combustibles, he dashed from the scene. At his party's heels, he raced on deck and clambered over *Philadelphia*'s rail to drop, safe, on *Intrepid*'s deck.

He looked back at the frigate then. Decatur still stood on her rail.

"Jump!" he cried.

Lieutenant Thorn seized his arm.

"We had a delay getting Charlie Morris's combustibles to him in the cockpit. Your fires may have spread so fast his party can't get out."

"Oh, no!"

The ketch's bow swung away from the frigate. Tom reached out.

Before he could wrench himself from the lieutenant's restraining clutch, he saw Charlie Morris's head on the spar deck by the forward hatchway . . . followed by eight others. Last members of the fire parties, they threw themselves into *Intrepid*'s rigging. Decatur followed, last.

Tom realized it had taken less than twenty minutes to board, seize, and fire the frigate—with no time to blow her bottom out. Flames already poured from her ports, threatening to envelop the ketch.

Sweeps in place, *Intrepid*'s oarsmen rowed desperately to escape the inferno.

Until now enemy shore guns had remained silent, their crews surprised, uncertain whether *Philadelphia*'s decks held friend or foe. But as *Intrepid* inched away from the burning frigate, the shouts of exultant boarders told the world they had accomplished their mission. Whereupon, Tripoli's shore batteries and ships, sure of their foe, blasted into action with 18- and 24-pounder guns.

In the bright light of the doomed frigate's blazing rigging, *Intrepid* made a perfect target. Worse, she lay in line with *Philadelphia*'s larboard broadside—which commanded the ketch's retreat passage . . . and, as her loaded guns heated, they fired over *Intrepid*'s masts.

With pilot Catalano at the wheel beside the quartermaster, powder-stained Decatur saw a lurid glare light the dark shadows of the old city of Tripoli.

"*Philadelphia*'s starboard broadside," he said lightly to Tom, "must be giving the Bashaw a taste of the same medicine."

Decatur laughed and Tom, despite the fact that a ball landed short of *Intrepid*'s stern and sent a fountain of water shimmering up between ketch and frigate, felt sudden relief.

In the overhanging cloud of smoke and reflected glow—in her death throes—*Philadelphia* looked victorious.

A light breeze now favored the seamen straining at *Intrepid*'s sweeps. And when, at the end of a half hour, the cannonading ceased, the ketch had taken only one shot—through her sail.

Tom looked back as the sky brightened and the roar of a tremendous explosion filled the harbor. *Philadelphia*'s magazines had blown up.

The frigate had died magnificently!

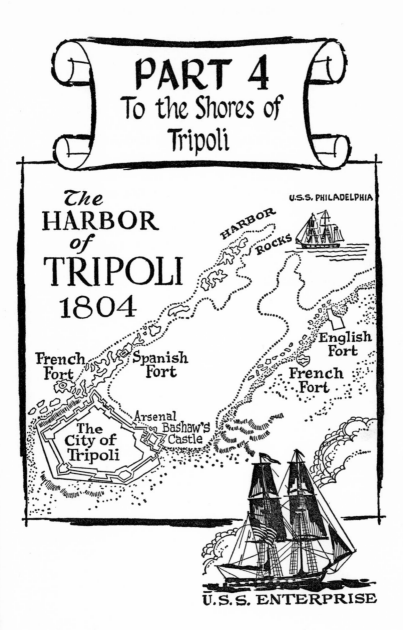

PART 4
To the Shores of Tripoli

The
HARBOR
of
TRIPOLI
1804

HARBOR ROCKS

U.S.S. PHILADELPHIA

English Fort

French Fort

French Fort   Spanish Fort

Arsenal
Bashaw's Castle

The City of Tripoli

U.S.S. ENTERPRISE

☆☆☆ CHAPTER 26

At news of Decatur's glorious exploit, the Governor of Sicily could not do enough to show his admiration. He passed the word to every ear on every vessel in the Bay of Syracuse, where the American Navy based, and he sent it by special messenger to the King at Naples. From there it spread like wildfire over Europe.

Together with his island's nobles, ladies, and gentlemen, the Governor staged a victory dinner for the officers and men of *Intrepid* and *Siren*.

At the gala dinner, held in one of Syracuse's most ornate palaces, Tom heard extravagant praise for the successful burning of the frigate. And after drinking more toasts than he thought possible, after eating more strange dishes than he dreamed could be concocted, and after listening to more speeches in more languages than he thought existed, Tom finally realized how nervously excited he'd felt before, during, and after the expedition. He couldn't make out for certain, however, which caused him greater nervousness—the expedition or the dinner.

Dressed in more gold braid and brilliant color than all the American officers put together, Sicily's governor read a message, which had come from Toulon, France, where British Admiral Horatio Nelson engaged in a blockade. Lord Nelson

147

lauded the destruction of *Philadelphia* as "the most bold and daring act of the age."

Called on, Decatur took the floor with a modesty that Tom knew came naturally. The Lieutenant simply did not think about fame when he went into action . . . fame sprang out of his affinity for excitement, afterward. Looking around at his officers, he told the dinner group:

"Every support that could be given, I received."

Tom blushed as midshipmen friends, applauding this, grinned at him.

Asking the expedition's seamen to rise in their seats, Decatur ended his short speech with an earnest wish:

"I trust," he said, "that the coolness and intrepidity of these brave men will ever characterize American sailors."

For Tom, Commodore Preble capped the evening.

When he rose to his feet, the Old Man's expression had lost its frost. His penetrating eyes still bored into everything he directed them on, but the upward curl of his lips softened their glare and seemed, also, to iron out the wrinkles on his sea-beaten cheeks.

"Your victory without loss of a man was miraculous," the Commodore opened, letting his gaze travel across the room to rest momentarily on every member of the raiding party. "Your conduct in the performance of the dangerous service assigned cannot be sufficiently estimated. It is beyond all praise."

To Tom's utter amazement, Commodore Preble then smiled and said, "I have asked the Secretary of the Navy to recommend to President Jefferson that Lieutenant Decatur be raised to captain."

At this the entire audience stood, applauding. Tom realized that he was not alone in his admiration for Decatur. The squadron rated him highly . . . the people of Syracuse looked on him as a hero.

The Commodore proceeded to hold his audience spellbound with a simple recital of what the American Navy sought to do in the Mediterranean. He offered the ideas that his young officers and sailors brought with them from the United States.

As the Commodore spoke, Tom felt patriotic Edward Preble's great warmth. Again he called his officers young cubs —his boys—and they liked it. Since the squadron had left home—each ship then a world of its own, its young commander eager to show his individual abilities—the captains had come to take pride in working together for their Old Man. Tom felt wonderful. He served in a great squadron under two great men, Edward Preble and Stephen Decatur.

In that moment Tom felt that no higher honor could ever befall him. He cherished every hard hour he'd put in—studying navigation, on watch, running errands, reprimanded, even mastheaded.

Commodore Preble laughed, and Tom came back to the banquet.

"You good people," the Commodore said, "may not appreciate the fact that my squadron's officers have denied you an excitement which, in earlier days on other stations, they felt they must provide whenever they went on shore. They have not engaged in a single duel!"

Commodore Preble bowed gratefully to his squadron.

"They've had too much else to keep them busy," he finished, realistically. "And this spring, heaven willing, they'll help me complete the job that the United States Navy came to the Mediterranean to do—wipe piracy off your sea."

As the Commodore sat down, the citizens of Syracuse rose in a standing ovation and for ten minutes clapped and cheered while Commodore Preble smiled and waved.

Tom Macdonough felt prouder than he'd ever felt in his life. Proud of the United States Navy and proud that he'd done a little something to show how much he, too, loved his country.

☆☆☆ CHAPTER 27

As Commodore Preble had indicated at the Syracuse banquet, he had in mind to hire or purchase from the King of the Two Sicilies three or four local gunboats, attach them to different vessels of his fleet, and "work with effect on Tripoli as soon as the spring opens." But spring of that year, 1804, lagged far behind.

On board *Enterprise,* Midshipman Macdonough meanwhile met storms off Tripoli, underwent a sultry and suffocating sirocco, helped keep Tripoline cruisers and gunboats from leaving port, and aided in destroying a merchant vessel that tried to run its cargo of salt through the blockade under cover of fog.

He heard enough of Commodore Preble's plans for bombarding Tripoli to ask "When?"

Decatur's unsatisfactory answer:

"When the Old Man has sufficient power to bring the Bashaw to his knees. He's still negotiating for those gunboats."

"How much longer will *that* take? It's already March!"

Decatur shrugged.

"How long does it take to get *anything* done in these parts?" he said. "You talk to Tony Barzullo who takes it up with Tony Farzullo . . . Farzullo gets in touch with Tony Marzullo . . . Marzullo sees a chance to throw some business to his brother-in-law Tony Parzullo, who has to bribe a friend in court named Tony Varzullo, whose second cousin is lady-in-waiting to a princess who will stage a reception at which she'll drop a word into the King's ear. Somewhere along the line three American consuls get involved, two of whom don't believe the project can succeed and, after the King listens, the word has to go back down the entire line."

Tom tried to laugh at Decatur's satire. But a picture of Rex Otis rotting in the Bashaw's prison for the long hot summer cut his laugh short.

While Tom champed the bit, waiting for the gunboats to materialize, the blockading vessels took their turn crossing to the Syracuse base for provisioning and shore liberty. Returning to the Tripoli blockade in late March, *Enterprise* stopped in Malta. On deck with the duty while Decatur and other officers went on shore, Tom watched a merchant brig flying American colors come into port and anchor. A half hour later a boat left the side of a nearby British frigate and rowed to the merchantman.

Tom looked on curiously. The boat stayed alongside the American brig for considerable time before shoving off. When it left, it carried one more man than when it arrived.

Sensing something up, Tom sent a midshipman over in the second gig to learn what went on. His hunch paid off. For the midshipman came back with news that the extra man had been impressed by the British boat despite the fact that the seaman had protection as an American citizen.

For a moment Tom almost panicked. He felt hot, then cold. What would Decatur do?

He knew very surely indeed what Decatur would do. With quiet determination, he did it. Ordering the gig armed, he got in and went after the British boat.

Heart pounding, he overtook the boat alongside the British warship, just as a seaman raised his boathook to make fast to the frigate. Though the British boat had eight oars and his gig had four only, he reached into the boat and hauled the American out. Bringing him to *Enterprise,* Tom waited—and took deep breaths to regain his poise.

Action followed fast. Red-faced with rage, the British frigate's captain stormed on board *Enterprise*—properly piped.

"You have dared take a man from one of His Majesty's boats," he announced pompously.

"That's right, sir," said Midshipman Macdonough. "I'll be happy to discuss my action with you, in the captain's cabin."

The visitor would have no part of that.

"I will take the man back with me," he shouted over the quarter-deck.

Tom stood easily now.

"I'm accountable to Captain Decatur for my conduct, not to you, sir," he said. "The man stays on board."

Furious, the visitor shouted louder.

"I will have the man if I have to haul my frigate alongside you!"

Tom bowed. "I suppose your frigate could sink our schooner," he replied. "But so long as *Enterprise* can swim, sir, we'll keep the man."

For several long seconds the captain glared. Tom fought to maintain his outward calm.

"You are a very young man and very indiscreet," declared the Britisher in something less than a bellow. "Suppose *I* had been in the boat when you came alongside. What would you have done?"

Tom breathed deep again. "I'd have taken the man, sir, or lost my life."

The captain showed utter disbelief.

"Would you attempt to stop me now if I impress men from that brig?"

"I would, sir," said Tom without raising his voice.

The captain visibly rocked.

Tom struck again, while he had the captain reeling.

"To convince yourself that I will, you have only to make the attempt."

"Well!"

Turning on his heel, the frustrated visitor angrily saluted the quarter-deck and descended *Enterprise*'s side.

Still quaking at the rail, Tom saw the British captain's boat bear toward the American brig. Ordering *Enterprise*'s gig manned again, he got into it, and waited.

While the British boat circled once around the brig, he stayed tense. When she continued rowing and returned to the frigate, he felt a tremendous relief.

Now he understood something of what Decatur must have felt when he went on board the xebec in Barcelona and said he'd cut off the discourteous guard's ears.

After Decatur returned that evening, Tom went to the captain's cabin and reported the incident briefly.

Decatur leaned back in his chair.

"Mister Macdonough," he said, "America's intention in the Mediterranean is to protect American seamen from piracy and from impressment. I commend your conduct in seeing to it that British captains, like everyone else in the Mediterranean at this time, treat the United States Navy with respect and courtesy."

Occasional shore leave at Syracuse between patrols provided pleasant hours with good food and good companions. Strolling casually along the waterfront on an unexpectedly balmy spring day, his Caribbean straw shading his bronzed face, Tom heard a peremptory hail from a sidewalk-cafe table.

"Come here, midshipman!"

Oh, oh! Tom saw two seated lieutenants—Richard Somers, commanding *Nautilus* and James Bruce Decatur, Stephen Decatur's young brother. Prepared for anything, including running an errand for their personal pleasure, Tom went to the table and stood at attention. Inured to hazing by lieutenants, he made no move, showed no annoyance.

Of a sudden, a sharp voice:

"How dare you wear my brother's hat!"

Tom froze, and strove to find a few temperate words with which to meet the accusation. Before he could find them, however, James Decatur held out his hand.

"Sit down. Steve told us about that hat of yours."

James Decatur acted as though he'd known, and liked, Tom all his life. Richard Somers, boyhood friend of Stephen Decatur, insisted that Tom eat with them.

Tom's pleasure showed. He took a seat at the officers' table as though accustomed to such august company.

"You're the man's kept Steve out of trouble with the Commodore over dueling."

Before Tom could deny any such good influence, James Decatur rambled on as if continuing a conversation begun long ago.

"You know, my father made Steve fight his first duel," he told Tom. "Steve had gone on board a merchantman in Philadelphia to get back some recruits he'd signed up for his frigate. He felt good about taking the stolen men off the merchantman, but Father told him that no Navy man should stand for the kind of verbal abuse he'd taken from the mate in doing it. So Steve went back, called the mate out, put a bullet in his hip, and won Father's congratulations."

Somers leaned across the table.

"That duel in *United States* wasn't Steve's fault. We'd been fooling around in midshipmen's mess, and he called me a fool. I nearly fell over when everyone insisted I should challenge him to a duel. Everyone else fell over when I challenged the whole berth instead."

Somers' infectious laugh warmed Tom.

"The first man hit me in the right arm and the second plugged me in the thigh. So Steve bandaged me, crouched down at my side, put his arm around me, and propped up my arm to hold the pistol steady. This time I wounded the other fellow." Somers laughed lightly. "So the rest of 'em called the affair off."

Tom nodded, wondering why the pair went into all this past history with him.

"We just want you to know that Steve's as big a man as you think he is," said Somers, answering Tom's unvoiced question.

"I've always known that!" Tom said.

Lieutenant Somers rose to leave with James Decatur.

"Then you belong to our club, and here's your initiation fee."

He dropped the bill for three meals in front of Tom, and departed arm-in-arm with James Decatur.

In April Commodore Preble went to Naples to meet with the King of the Two Sicilies. Their face-to-face talks produced results: the King loaned what the Commodore offered to buy —six gunboats and two bomb vessels.

Lateen-rigged, fifty-six-and-a-half feet overall with 18-foot beam and 4½-foot draft, each gunboat carried a long iron 24-pounder in its bow and thirty-five men. Each bomb vessel, about thirty tons, carried a 13-inch brass sea mortar and forty men. For each of the eight vessels, the King provided twelve Neapolitan bombardiers, gunners, and sailors to help fight the craft.

Commodore Preble warned his officers not to expect too much of the gunboats. Heavy, flat-bottomed, they rowed and sailed abominably. In fact, the Commodore wryly admitted, the boats had been built for the defense of harbors, not for sea duty; the squadron would have to tow them over to Tripoli.

"They were the best I could get," he told his captains without apology, adding, "I thought it for the good of our service to employ them—particularly as the weather in July and August is generally pleasant and without them our force is too small to make any impression on Tripoli."

In his easy way, Decatur briefed his officers on how the newly-acquired vessels would add to the fighting strength of flagship *Constitution,* the three schooners *Enterprise, Nautilus, Vixen,* and the three brigs *Argus, Siren,* and *Scourge*—former British warship *Transfer* which, sold to the Bashaw, had fallen captive to *Vixen* while trying to reach Tripoli from Malta.

"The schooners and the brigs will help the squadron create an impression of great power," he pointed out. "Actually, they'll help very little in breaking down harbor defenses, since they can't get close enough to do much damage with their short-range carronades."

He further pointed out:

"The gunboats and the bomb vessels will do the decisive fighting."

He let that sink in. Finally:

"The flagship's long guns should have good overall effect."

As Tom saw the picture, some twelve hundred Americans would take on twenty-five thousand Turks and Arabs. While *Constitution* battered at Tripoli's heavily fortified walls, the unwieldy gunboats would carry the burden of the fight to the Tripoline navy which boasted a brig, two schooners, two large galleys, and nineteen gunboats.

As if seeing inside Tom's mind, Decatur asked his officers what chance they thought the bombardment had of succeeding.

Lieutenant Bainbridge, who knew Decatur of old, laughed.

"The odds seem just about right!"

In the days that followed, Tom often wondered how boastful you can get and still live up to your fine words. For if Joe Bainbridge thought the American squadron, with the King's flat-bottomed scows for support, could subdue Tripoli . . . well, Bainbridge had optimism to spare.

For his part, Tom found the gunboats hard to grow fond of. Commissioned 29 May, at Messina, they sailed and rowed as poorly as the Commodore predicted.

The six craft formed two divisions of three boats each. Lieutenant Somers commanded the first division, in Number One boat; Lieutenant James Decatur captained Number Two boat, and Lieutenant Joshua Blake captained Number Three.

Stephen Decatur commanded the second division, in Number Four boat, which also carried Midshipman Macdonough; Lieutenant Bainbridge captained Number Five; Lieutenant John Trippe, from *Vixen*, captained Number Six.

Together, and by divisions, the gunboats spent most of June practicing maneuvers. Under sail and oars, sometimes under both, they drilled whenever the continually foul weather permitted.

Gun captain on the second division's Number Four boat, Tom watched its crew—Americans and Neapolitans—wrestle their craft through its paces by brute strength. At the end of the month he had no qualms about the ability of his gunners to shoot; but how much practice, he still wondered, would it take to cope with the craft's deficiencies? Did Commodore Preble still think he could transform these flat-bottomed impossible-to-sail tubs into a bombardment force?

With Midshipman Macdonough still depressed and pessimistic, Commodore Edward Preble led the American squadron out of Syracuse, 14 July, towing the gunboats. After stopping at Malta, the flagship sighted Tripoli, 25 July.

Off the city, storms kept the squadron inactive for the next nine days.

☆☆☆ CHAPTER 28

During those nine days, while the squadron lay off the coast of Tripoli, Tom had ample opportunity to count his sins, write a long letter home, and mull over how and when he'd ever make lieutenant. He counted his sins quickly, took longer to write the letter to Hester, and dwelt at considerable length on the mysterious way in which the Navy worked to perform its miracles of promotions.

Certainly he'd put in plenty of time—more than four years, most of it at sea—and he'd learned his job well. From the way Decatur gave him his head, he could very well step into a lieutenant's shoes on any vessel in the squadron and fill them more than satisfactorily. Too, he'd had several chances to show his quality—the incident at Malta with the British captain had brought approval from the entire fleet. And Commodore Preble knew, at least, that he still existed.

Standing watch in a squall, rain beating down fit to drive through his oilskins, Tom experienced an unexpected insight.

"How sorry can you get for yourself?" he heard in the passing storm. His own voice.

"What other midshipman's had a promotion? Charlie Morris, who beat you on board *Philadelphia* that night? Rex Otis in the Bashaw's dungeon? Joe Calkins and Joe Robins of *Ganges,* struck down in the Caribbean by yellow jack?"

Then:

"Count your blessings!" he told himself in the serious manner of Caesar Rodney. "You're lucky to be alive . . . and luckier to be going up against the Turks under a couple of officers such as Preble and Decatur."

He nodded.

"Amen," he heard himself say in his own subdued voice, "so be it."

He hadn't enjoyed his mood of the past month, grousing about the cumbersome gunboats and the aromatic Neapolitans who served so cheerfully in gunboat Number Four. Already he felt better.

On 3 August, a memorable day for the United States Navy and for Midshipman Macdonough, Commodore Edward Preble found conditions favorable for an attack on the city of Tripoli.

From *Constitution*'s quarter-deck he signaled his captains to begin their work of bringing the Bashaw to a full realization that his days of piracy had passed. Flying the national colors from the peak of her spanker gaff and the Commodore's broad pennant from her mizzentop, the flagship led the squadron toward the long-blockaded harbor.

As *Enterprise* towed Number Four gunboat into the bay of Tripoli, Tom grew increasingly tense.

Fighting ship-against-ship . . . at a distance . . . with big guns, could not compare with fighting in a little galley . . . with a handful of companions . . . in an enemy harbor defended to the teeth. Too, the element of surprise had helped the Americans in the raid on *Philadelphia*.

Now the Turks stood ready and waiting at their guns. And, under the city's batteries, nineteen enemy gunboats lay alerted, with a brass howitzer on each quarter and, forward, a copper gun nearly twelve feet long that could fire a 29-pound ball.

At 2 P.M., Commodore Preble signaled the schooners and brigs to cast off the gunboats and bomb vessels . . .

At 2:30, he signaled the small boats to advance and attack . . .

At 2:45, the bomb vessels' mortars began to shell the city and *Constitution*'s big guns opened fire on Tripoli's walls.

Under cover of this barrage, the two American gunboat divisions moved in on fourteen Tripoline galleys which, in two divisions also, came out beyond a line of sheltering rocks. Five other Turk gunboats stayed behind the rocks, in reserve.

Using sails and oars, the six American boats advanced on the enemy's eastern division. But their line quickly broke:

Number One boat could not work far enough to windward to stay with the others. Lieutenant Somers therefore bore down single-handed on the enemy's western division of five gunboats . . .

Number Three boat caught sight of a recall signal mistakenly flown on the flagship. Lieutenant Blake accordingly left the line . . .

Number Five boat, having lost a lateen yard while in tow, could not keep up with her companions. Lieutenant Bainbridge therefore had to content himself with doing what damage he could at long range . . .

The remaining gunboat captains made for the enemy's eastern division of nine boats—Lieutenant James Decatur in boat Number Two, and Lieutenant Blake in boat Number Six, led by Stephen Decatur in boat Number Four.

When the Turks opened fire, the action swept Tom up like a straw in a cyclone. His boat, and its two companions, replied at grapeshot distance, their 24-pounders showering small shot and their marines showering musket balls. The three boats continued to close.

Almost before Tom knew what happened, Number Four grappled fast to an enemy gunboat and he leaped into it with Decatur, flailing with his cutlass as the crew followed. Decatur led the charge around one side of the midships hatchway. Tom led around the other.

For the second time, as on *Philadelphia*'s spar deck, he faced the enemy man-to-man. For the second time, too, he saw pikes and tomahawks in use.

The Turks, confident in the power of their numbers and

believing themselves invincible in hand-to-hand fighting, made a determined resistance. Shouting weirdly, they stoutly defended themselves with muskets and spears.

But the Americans, trained for weeks in boarding, countered with Indian war whoops as they swung tomahawks and fought with fury pent up by long months of frustrating inaction. In a bold and bloody struggle that lasted twenty minutes, they justified Lieutenant Bainbridge's optimism about the odds. They forced the Tripolines to their knees.

Glowing, Tom stood there, blood-spattered, clothes ripped, and took his first chance to look around as they brought their prize out in tow.

Over the harbor he saw signs of American success:

Assisted by the carronades of the brigs and schooners, Lieutenant Somers in Number One boat had forced the enemy's western division to retire behind the rocks . . .

Joined by Lieutenant Blake in Number Three, Lieutenant Bainbridge in Number Five kept up an effective, though distant, fire against the enemy fleet . . .

Lieutenant Trippe had run Number Six alongside one of the enemy's largest boats, boarded with only a midshipman and nine seamen and, Tom later learned, fought at odds of 36 to 11. Though Trippe himself sustained eleven saber wounds, several severe, his party had cleared the decks and hauled the enemy's colors down . . .

James Decatur in Number Two boat still engaged an enemy . . .

The bomb vessels kept up their steady shelling . . .

The brigs and schooners held back the enemy's reserve division of gunboats . . .

The frigate continued to pound the city's batteries.

As Tom watched, the wind now shifted, the enemy's boats dispersed, and the flagship signaled for gunboats and bomb vessels to retire from action.

A sense of tremendous accomplishment flowed through

Midshipman Macdonough. Returning to earth from what now seemed like a dream, he realized how tired he felt and how bedraggled he must look. He'd done his part of a good job, done it well, and he wanted now to clean up and talk about the day's details at length.

But the day had not ended for him. He had more fighting to do.

☆☆☆ CHAPTER 29

As his boat turned toward *Constitution,* he heard the bad news —passed by the midshipman commanding Lieutenant James Decatur's Number Two boat, which drew up.

Number Two boat had subdued her foe, who struck her colors. When, however, the lieutenant boarded the surrendered vessel to take possession, her crazed Turk captain had treacherously shot him through the head! Tom saw James Decatur, on Number Two's deck, dying.

Tom turned to face Stephen Decatur. As he caught Decatur's eye, without a command from anyone, Number Four boat's company bent to their oars in pursuit of the murderers.

The chase carried the American boat close under Tripoli's batteries where the fleeing galley, unable to man her sweeps, barely moved through the water. Ranging alongside, Number Four boat grappled.

Decatur leaped on board the galley. With him leaped Tom and thirteen seamen, to meet thirty-odd Turks.

Tom no longer felt tired. His strength had returned a hundredfold. He burned with ice-cold rage. And though the previous fighting had seemed to demand all his powers—physical, mental, and emotional—this fresh hand-to-hand encounter called out unsuspected reserves.

When the first turbaned Turk he met lunged with a long esponton, he warded the spear off with his cutlass. But his blade broke at the hilt and over his right shoulder he glimpsed the descending butt of a Turkish musket. He moved instinctively.

Leaning forward to lessen the blow, he grabbed the musket butt as it fell and wrenched the gun from the Turk's hands. Swinging the musket high, he crashed its barrel against the temple of the man with the esponton. In almost the same swing, he laid the gun barrel alongside the skull of the still astounded Turk from whom he'd wrested it, and heard a second crunch of smashed bone.

A dozen feet from him, two men writhed on the deck. Decatur, the underneath man, his arm and breast oozing blood, wrestled a Turk and came up on top as a second Turkish officer raised his saber. Tom rushed to parry the blow.

But he couldn't cover the distance in time. Helpless, he saw the blade fall as a bleeding American seaman, powerless to use his numbed arms, thrust his head between Decatur and the dropping scimitar. Tom's musket butt batted the attacking Turk across the deck where he toppled over the rail into the water—dead before the sea closed above him.

When Tom looked back, another Turk had fallen on Decatur and was reaching for the yataghan in the sash around his waist. With his left hand Decatur pinned the hand that held the short, curved knife. At the same time, he reached his right hand into his pantaloons pocket to cock his pistol. Through the pocket, Decatur fired into his assailant's stomach.

As Tom reached him, Decatur sprang to his feet, covered with blood yet ready to continue the fight. But the Turks wanted no more. For the second time, to the second brother, the Tripoline gunboat surrendered.

Decatur expressed no direct thanks to Tom. Instead, he honored him with the mission of presenting to Commodore Preble, on board *Constitution,* the flags of the two gunboats Tom had helped vanquish.

From the Commodore himself, Midshipman Macdonough learned the total results of the American bombardment:

Constitution had considerably damaged the city's batteries, at the expense of slight damage aloft . . .

The squadron's guns had sunk three gunboats in the harbor . . .

The gunboats had captured three Tripoline galleys in the hand-to-hand fighting . . .

The first bombardment of Tripoli had cost the United States Navy one dead—James Decatur.

☆☆☆ CHAPTER 30

To the squadron next morning, Edward Preble promulgated a general order:

> The Commodore deeply regrets the death of the brave Lieutenant James Decatur, who nobly fell at the moment he had obliged an enemy of superior force to strike to him.

With appropriate rites and musket volleys, the body of Decatur's brother slid from *Constitution*'s gangway into the waters of the Mediterranean. Midshipman Macdonough watched solemnly.

With equal gravity he accompanied Stephen Decatur, when,

after inspecting *Enterprise* following the burial ceremony, the captain stopped in sick bay.

"How's Reuben James doing?" Decatur asked.

Surgeon Heerman looked puzzled.

"I've got a Thomas James here," he said; "no Reuben James."

"I want to see the man who put his head between me and the Turk's saber yesterday."

"Oh!" The surgeon nodded. "You mean Daniel Frashier. He's the one most carved up. Two gashes in the head, one severe. Also one deep cut across the wrist and seven wounds about the hands. But I think he'll make it." The surgeon took Decatur to the cot of a much-bandaged seaman.

Frashier smiled wanly. Decatur put a comforting hand on his shoulder.

"Commodore Preble knows what you did, Daniel," said Decatur, "and I shall never forget it!"

To Tom it looked as though Daniel Frashier, wounds and bandages notwithstanding, would take on more Turks that very minute if Decatur asked.

Standing at *Enterprise*'s taffrail following inspection, Tom gazed over distant Tripoli with considerable emotion.

What would the Bashaw do now—come to terms or stubbornly hold out until the squadron brought his castle down around his ears in rubble? How would the Bashaw treat the prisoners in his dungeons—put them out on the castle walls to face the bombardment fire or let them die in their cells when the walls tumbled?

How would Commodore Preble move next, having given the Bashaw a hearty taste of American determination to wipe piracy off the Mediterranean Sea?

Tom knew what *he* wanted—surrender. It would accomplish the squadron's aim—end Tripolitan raids on shipping. It would avoid further killing. It would free *Philadelphia*'s company.

Above all, Tom wanted to get Rex out of the Bashaw's clutches. More and more, he missed his old berthmate ... more than he'd realized or imagined possible. From the afternoon when the pair had hauled *Ganges'* jolly-boat crew out of the New Castle tavern, his affection for the mad midshipman had mounted steadily, almost daily.

"He's as crazy as any Turk," Tom found himself muttering, and he laughed at the thought that by this time Rex undoubtedly had invented a way of driving his captors even wilder.

Watching a small boat shove off from the flagship, Tom pictured *Constitution* leading yesterday's squadron into the harbor. He relived the fighting, and visualized how he'd missed death by very little. How often could he count on such good luck? Every time Number Four boat engaged the enemy? Next time? The time after?

Constitution's boat discharged a man at *Enterprise*'s ladder, and Tom flinched as he looked down. He'd never seen such a gaunt human—so thin that, as the country saying went, he'd have to stand twice in the same place to cast a shadow. The man saluted the quarter-deck, and Tom saw his face.

"Rex!" Eyes nearly filled with tears, he raced to the gangway and threw his arms around his berthmate.

Rex grinned. "Got a spare hammock on board this craft?"

Tom turned away to hide his emotion.

That day and later in midshipmen's mess, Rex gave only odds and ends of his experiences after *Philadelphia*'s capture—as if he never wanted to remember them.

Yes, he'd seen the Bashaw, just once.

"A big man, about five-feet-ten, and fat," he said, "looking tawdry and splendid at the same time, in a bright-blue robe embroidered with a little gold and a lot of tinsel. Wore a broad belt decorated with diamonds and carried two gold-mounted pistols in it, along with a saber on a gold chain."

No, he had no idea whether the Bashaw would give in or fight it out ...

Yes, Captain Bainbridge and Consul Nissen had done all they could for *Philadelphia*'s company, but the Turks treated them like slaves and fed them like slaves . . .

No, he did *not* relish Arab food!

"Would I look like this if I did?"

How had he escaped? Well, that would take hours to detail. In a few words, he told Tom:

"When you fellows bombarded the city yesterday, I clobbered a guard on the head with a spade. Then clambered over the prison wall and ran like the devil. Near the waterfront I hid in an empty cask behind a warehouse."

How did he get to the squadron?

"After dark, I found a wreck of a boat with two holes and a broken oar. I just plugged the holes with my stockings and paddled out of the harbor. On *Constitution,* the Old Man saw to it that I got all the food I could stuff and all the sleep I could crowd into a few hours."

Then what?

Rex replied like his old bantering self.

"Well, figuring the Old Man had done a favor by feeding me, I told him I'd like to pay him back by fighting where the action's bound to be hottest the next time he moves in to bombard the city."

Rex paused and eyed Tom, who refused to fall into the old trap.

"When the Old Man asked me where I thought the hottest action would be," finished Rex, "I told him just to put me in the same ship with that peerless midshipman, Thomas Macdonough of Delaware, and we'd find it!"

On 5 August, Commodore Preble sent a French privateer, brought to by *Argus,* back into Tripoli harbor with fourteen Turks wounded in the first bombardment.

The squadron used the time of waiting to repair damages received in the first attack. The squadron also refitted the three

captured Tripoline gunboats, which became U.S. gunboats
Numbers Seven, Eight, Nine, under command of Lieutenants
William Montgomery Crane of *Vixen*, Jonathon Thorn of
Enterprise, and James R. Caldwell of *Siren.*

The French privateer returned with a letter from the Bashaw
who said he would accept reasonable peace terms. The Bashaw
requested the Commodore to send an American boat into
Tripoli under a flag of truce.

When, however, no white flag rose over the Bashaw's castle
to confirm the arrangement, the Commodore prepared a
second assault on Tripoli ". . . designed to bring the enemy to
a proper sense of their situation."

☆☆☆ CHAPTER 31

On 7 August, at 9 A.M., the squadron then lying about six
miles off the city, *Constitution* signaled the gunboats, the
mortar vessels, the brigs, and the schooners to stand in for the
second assault.

By 2 P.M., the flagship, the brigs, and the schooners had
taken up a position where they could drive back the Tripoline
gunboats should the Turks seek to come out from behind the
harbor's guarding rocks.

At half past two Commodore Preble signaled the assault.

To silence a battery of seven heavy guns which covered the
approach to a small bay westward of the harbor, the gunboats
led . . .

To take a position in this bay where they could shell the

city easily but where only a few enemy guns could bear on them, the bomb vessels followed . . .

While the frigate, the brigs, and the schooners kept Tripoline gunboats boxed in behind the rocks—driving them back as they made successive attempts to slip out . . . while the bomb vessels proceeded to shell the city . . . the gunboats took on the brunt of the action.

Instead of fighting Turks hand-to-hand as he had in the first attack, Midshipman Macdonough found himself busy helping fire Number Four's 24-pounder at a shore battery. Danger loomed just as great, however, and both gunboat divisions suffered considerable damage in the first hour.

At 3:30 P.M., a moment after Tom had pulled Rex Otis away from the gunwale to yell an order from Decatur into his ear, a 24-pound ball plowed through Number Four's deck where Rex had stood. Tom had time only to make sure the hole lay well above the waterline before he heard a terrific explosion.

Turning, he saw Lieutenant Caldwell's Number Nine boat, sinking. An enemy hot shot had struck her magazine. On her shattered deck men lay dead or stunned by the blast. The boat, Tom saw at a glance, could not stay afloat for more than a few minutes.

But—even as the boat sank—Midshipman Robert Spence, son of *Philadelphia*'s purser, now held prisoner by the Bashaw, superintended the loading of her gun. Tom saw Spence's gun crew fire their 24-pounder for the last time, give three cheers as the boat went down under them, and swim toward Number Four with their wounded.

By 5:30 P.M.—when the flagship signaled the gunboats and bomb vessels to retire, and the squadron withdrew to its anchorage—the American gunboats had pounded six of the battery's seven guns into silence and almost entirely destroyed its walls.

Regathering his personal forces after the day's excitement,

Tom felt a sense of accomplishment again—along with a realization that the Bashaw, with other batteries and other walls, could hold out a long time yet.

"But he doesn't rank with the Commodore in pure stubbornness," Rex pointed out.

"Meaning?"

"Like John Paul Jones, the Old Man's just begun to fight."

"So we can look forward to more of what we had today?"

"Exactly!"

To Tom it seemed as though Rex saw the situation with reasonable clarity. Given time, the squadron could, and would, batter all of Tripoli's walls down as the gunboats had crumbled the battery's.

But that same evening the blow fell.

Corvette *John Adams* joined the squadron from the United States, and Captain Isaac Chauncey delivered dispatches to the effect that four frigates, arriving soon, would bring Captain Samuel Barron, senior in rank, to supersede Commodore Preble as commander of the Mediterranean fleet!

Decatur voiced the squadron's feelings:

"We'll have to pound the Bashaw to terms before Barron arrives!"

Tom took the turn of events especially hard. What kind of justice came out of the Navy Department? First, Secretary Smith warmly praised Commodore Preble for his accomplishments thus far . . . then, recall before the Old Man had finished the job he'd set out to do! Even the captain's commission that came for Stephen Decatur (dated back to the burning of *Philadelphia*), did not compensate for the bad news.

Mirroring the squadron's sentiment, Commodore Preble pushed operations against Tripoli with all vigor. But troubles piled up. Lack of water and shortage of men harassed the captains . . . worthless stores and resulting scurvy struck officers and men alike . . . storms threatened to capsize the gunboats.

Despite all, the squadron stubbornly maintained the blockade. And, the morning of 10 August, the French consul hoisted a white flag on the consulate's flagstaff—under his national colors—to signal that the Bashaw would treat with Commodore Preble . . .

The Commodore sent a boat into the harbor. With it went letters for imprisoned Captain Bainbridge . . .

In the afternoon, the boat returned with a message advising that the Bashaw, on receipt of $500 for each American prisoner he held, would terminate the war . . .

Commodore Preble laughed at the offer—$350,000 less than the Bashaw had demanded before the first two American bombardments. How much would he lower it after the next?

Things picked up.

On 20 August, ketch *Intrepid* arrived from Syracuse with fresh water, vegetables, and provisions . . .

The weather finally cleared . . .

Everyone felt better, including Midshipman Macdonough.

☆☆☆ CHAPTER 32

Almost three weeks had passed since the second assault on Tripoli. And anticipation of action after so long a wait, combined with a feeling that time had almost run out on their Commodore, filled the squadron. Tom sensed it on all sides. Officers snapped orders incisively . . . seamen responded smartly.

With word that the third assault would take place in the dark, Tom appreciated that the Old Man had begun to reach into his tactics bag for every trick it held. The third assault would provide a surprise punch.

At 8 P.M., 24 August, the squadron anchored about two and a half miles off Tripoli's batteries.

At 12 o'clock, the mortar vessels and gunboats moved in under cover of midnight.

At 2 A.M., *Constitution, John Adams,* the brigs, and the schooners joined their great guns with those of the bomb vessels and gunboats in the surprise bombardment.

At daylight, having blasted the city, the squadron retired and awaited the Bashaw's response.

When the next four days brought no word—nor any sign of the frigates from home, with the new commodore—pressure mounted. Like every officer in the fleet, Tom found himself working up to high pitch. The squadron *must* bring the Bashaw to his knees before the frigates appeared on the horizon.

That Edward Preble's determined campaign against the Bashaw finally had inspired President Jefferson to send what the Commodore so often had requested—a force large enough to bring the war to a quick close—only filled everyone with a desire to snatch the victory with the force in hand.

As Tom put it to Rex:

"*Our* squadron's done the dirty work. We don't need anybody else to help finish what we've started!"

The fourth assault—its chief target the Bashaw's castle—began at 1:30 A.M., 29 August, after an evening of intense preparation.

The gunboats sailed and rowed close to the harbor's rocks, taking a position within grape-shot distance of the castle.

With them (instead of the bomb vessels, so damaged in earlier actions that they could not take part in this) went all small boats of the squadron, manned and armed to assist in boarding the enemy's gunboats.

Nearby, to support the attacking force, the schooners and the brigs kept under way.

At 3 A.M., within pistol shot of the rocks, the gunboats opened a heavy fire on city, batteries, castle, and ships in the harbor.

How much damage Number Four boat did that night, Tom never found out. He only knew that his boat expended all its ammunition and that, while no Tripoline gunboat came near enough to board, the Turks sent Number Four a warm return fire.

At 5:30 A.M., when *Constitution* ordered the brigs and schooners to retire the gunboats from action in tow, Tom rode out of the harbor behind *Enterprise*. Excited and exhausted, he then watched the flagship stand into the harbor and take over as if determined, like her commander, to end the war then and there.

Constitution poured her great shot into Tripoli's gunboats, sinking one, disabling two, and causing the remainder to retreat . . .

She then ran well into the harbor, came up within musket shot of the batteries on the mole, and poured round shot, grape, and canister into the city . . .

At 6:15 A.M., Commodore Preble finally hauled off, leaving Tripoli's capital a shambles.

Now the Bashaw could feel safe neither by day nor by night! Would he capitulate, Tom asked himself, suing for peace on the Commodore's terms, before Barron arrived?

For five days more the squadron anxiously watched the French consul's flagstaff. When it flew no white flag, the squadron girded for a fifth assault.

"It's now or never," said Tom.

Rex nodded, with surprising solemnity.

☆☆☆ CHAPTER 33

During the days of waiting for a signal from Tripoli's Bashaw, Tom had kept physically busy repairing Number Four gunboat and getting fresh ammunition on board. But he had a good deal of time to think, too.

He'd developed since joining *Ganges* at New Castle. Only four years ago? Four years of hard and concentrated study . . . four years learning how to sail and shoot . . . four years observing men's characters. He felt grown up now. He could hold his own with anyone, for he had worked with, played with, fought alongside the best.

Where else could he have found friends like the midshipmen he'd met in *Ganges* and *Constellation* and *Philadelphia* and *Constitution* and *Enterprise*? Where could he have learned so much about wind and water but under such salty skippers as John Mullowney and Alexander Murray and William Bainbridge? Who but Edward Preble and Stephen Decatur could have shown him, by their own self-discipline and love of country, how to conduct himself as the Navy's greats—if the opportunity ever came his way?

Tom felt very proud of his schooling, and very grateful. He would do anything to bring victory to the squadron. He understood now how his father must have felt when he gave up doctoring, buckled on a sword, and led soldiers in the Revolution to fight for their country's freedom. Like his father, he sought American freedom from tyranny. His father had refused to bow to a British king; he refused to bow to a Barbary bashaw.

Leaks caulked and mortar beds made tight again, the fleet's two bomb vessels rejoined the squadron the afternoon of 3 September, when it moved in to attack Tripoli for the fifth time.

At 3:30 the bomb vessels gained an effective position and began to shell the city . . .

Enemy gunboats had worked to windward along the harbor's eastern side outside the rocks off Fort English. To combat this maneuver, calculated to prevent the Americans from running very far into the harbor without leaving the enemy in their rear, Commodore Preble ordered both gunboat divisions to attack to windward. With *Argus, Enterprise, Nautilus, Siren,* and *Vixen,* they reached close to the rocks. Here Lieutenant Somers' division, with the brigs and schooners, opened fire on the fort . . .

Under Decatur, the second division closed with the enemy.

For an hour, the American boats engaged with their guns, unable to board. Elusive, avoiding hand-to-hand conflict, the Turks kept their galleys at respectful gun shot distance. With grim satisfaction, Tom realized that the pirates wanted no part of pikes and tomahawks swung by seamen who cared little for Turkish espontons and yataghans.

The Tripolines showed such great respect for American ability to fight at the close quarters which previously they had considered their own specialty that Tom wondered if this indicated a recognition on the Bashaw's part that his time had come?

Or did it indicate new caution?

Or—Tom felt a sudden chill—did it mean that the Bashaw had got wind of Captain Barron's arrival to replace Commodore Preble and looked on the newcomer as an easier antagonist and now played for time?

What could the Old Man do about that?

While he helped Number Four's crew at their 24-pounder,

Tom saw *Constitution* run down past the exposed mortar vessels which continued to pour their bombs into Tripoli.

Tom watched, fascinated. What was the Commodore up to? Had he sensed what Tom had felt? If so, what trick had he found in the bottom of that bag of his to administer the death blow? Hit and run? He certainly couldn't plan to— he did! As calmly as if staging target practice on open sea, the frigate turned into the wind. And with everyone else in the squadron, Tom cheered.

The Old Man intended personally to stand and slug it out with the Bashaw here and now. He was taking the flagship up to the very mouths of the shore guns!

Coming to handsomely, her big guns belched a broadside into the city. Tom saw tons of metal wreak destruction in the batteries and the castle. He saw too that the enemy's return fire damaged only *Constitution*'s sails and rigging—with no visible effect on her hull. "Old Ironsides" her men called her. That she was!

Deliberately Old Ironsides stood and, deliberately, fired again. Commodore Edward Preble threw a total of eleven broadsides into the city.

Falling away then, at 4:30 P.M., the flagship signaled the gunboats to retire in tow. And when Number Four boat made her line fast to *Enterprise*'s stern, Tom knew that the squadron had completed its job.

Sweaty, grimy, he looked up to catch Decatur's eye. In a spontaneous gesture that reflected his affection, his thanks for all Decatur had done for him, Tom took off his battered straw hat and swept it across his chest like a salaam. Smiling with equal affection, Decatur touched the brim of his equally weather-beaten straw in a brief acknowledging salute.

Herding her fleet before her, one month exactly since the squadron's first bombardment, U.S. flagship *Constitution*, Commodore Edward Preble, sailed out of Tripoli harbor like a conqueror.

Only one more move remained, next day. With twelve other volunteers including Rex Otis, Lieutenant Somers took ketch *Intrepid,* one hundred barrels of powder, and two hundred and fifty shells under the city's walls as a floating mine. Anticipating the odds against their return, Dick Somers had told Decatur:

"If the enemy boards us before we reach the city, we'll put a match to the magazine."

Intrepid entered the harbor at 8 P.M., 4 September, with a leading breeze from the eastward. As she approached her destination, Tom heard shots from the city's batteries . . . followed by a terrific explosion and a stunning silence. Rex?

Not a single Tripoline gun fired during the rest of the night. And at sunrise, 5 September, the squadron could sight nothing of *Intrepid*. One of the enemy's largest gunboats also had vanished. Three others—greatly damaged—lay on shore. Only Captain Bainbridge, prisoner in the Bashaw's castle, ever saw the mangled bodies of the men who struck the squadron's final blow against Tripoli.

That same day came orders to strip gunboats and bomb vessels of their guns, mortars, balls, and shells. Tom supervised the work on Number Four, with mixed emotions. What now?

He learned very soon.

☆☆☆ CHAPTER 34

Decatur called Tom to the captain's cabin the following morning.

"I have a signal from Commodore Preble requesting your

presence on board *Constitution,*" said Decatur. "But before you call on the Commodore, I want to take the opportunity, Midshipman Macdonough, to say that you have attended to your duty in this ship with the greatest of efficiency and loyalty. I thank you."

Rising, he held out his hand.

"Good luck to you, Tom."

Tom found only three words to express his feelings.

"Thank *you,* Steve," he said, taking Decatur's hand and turning abruptly.

In the second gig's stern sheets as grizzled seamen rowed him toward the flagship, Tom sensed that he could expect almost anything from this call on Commodore Preble. He'd reached a turning point in his life. Saluting the quarter-deck, he presented himself to the officer on duty.

"Midshipman Macdonough requests permission to come on board," he said.

"Yes, sir!" replied Midshipman Morris. Charlie hid a broad wink from the others on deck. "Seaman Wallace, you will escort Mister Macdonough to the Commodore."

In the big cabin, Commodore Edward Preble signed a paper that lay on top of the pile on his mahogany desk. He looked tired, but he also looked a man who'd done what he set out to do. He raised his head, motioned Tom to a seat in front of the desk, his eyes frosty as usual. Tom waited.

The Commodore's words came slowly.

"You will proceed shortly to Syracuse with the squadron," he said, "while *Constitution* stays here with *Argus* and *Vixen.* Before you go, I want you to know that I've had my eye on you for a long time, son . . ."

Tom felt a sudden flow of emotion that threatened to make him as limp as he'd felt in Decatur's cabin. Son! Why, the Old Man did indeed consider him one of his boys!

" . . . I know everything you've done . . . against *Philadelphia* and against enemy gunboats. I hope you take as great pride in your work as I take in it. Because, whether you realize it or not, this squadron of ours has helped the United States do more to discourage piracy in the Mediterranean than all Christendom has done in the past three hundred years."

The Commodore lifted from his desk the paper he'd signed after Tom came into the cabin. He handed it across the desk.

Tom took the paper. He saw its bottom lines first:

"Given under my hand on board the U.S. ship *Constitution* off Tripoly the 6th day of Sept. 1804 . . . Edwd. Preble."

Above the signature he saw his own name, and he read the body of the page:

Sir:
You are hereby appointed Lieutenant of the
U.S. Schooner *Enterprise*. You will therefore
repair on board said schooner, and take upon
yourself the charge and duty of Lieutenant
agreeable to the regulations of the service,
for which this shall be your sufficient
authority.

Decatur's lieutenant! Tom could remember only, afterward, that Commodore Preble stood up, took his hand, and said:

"The best of fortune attend you, Lieutenant Macdonough, wherever future service in the United States Navy may place you."